Margaret Dukes

7th March 1946.

NELSON'S AEROSCIENCE MANUALS

GENERAL EDITOR :

H. LEVY, M.A., D.Sc., F.R.S.E.

ELEMENTARY STATISTICS

ELEMENTARY STATISTICS

by

HYMAN LEVY M.A. D.Sc. F.R.S.E.

Professor of Mathematics
Imperial College of Science London

and

E. E. PREIDEL M.Sc. A.R.C.S. D.I.C.

Assistant Lecturer in Mathematics
Imperial College of Science London

THOMAS NELSON AND SONS LTD
LONDON EDINBURGH PARIS MELBOURNE
TORONTO AND NEW YORK

First published September 1944
Reprinted 1945

PREFACE

THE study of statistics is at last taking its rightful place in the educational scheme. This is as true for engineers, physicists, chemists, biologists, and mathematicians as for those concerned with the social sciences. Indeed, a good deal of the preliminary ground, including probability, may be broken even at the school stage.

This little book covers part of the work on statistics and probability which has been taught at the Imperial College of Science to students of mathematics and physics and to many biologists during the past twenty years. More recently it has found its way into the syllabus of first-year engineering students.

Readers whose knowledge of mathematics is only moderate may find Chapter VI, on the Accuracy of the Mean, beyond their capacity, although there is, in fact, no appeal to anything beyond the most elementary algebra. On a first reading, therefore, this chapter may be omitted, providing the conclusion arrived at is fully understood. It finds its application principally in the chapter on Quality Control (Chapter XIV), a subject vital for production engineers.

No topic can be dealt with by theory alone. Experimental methods on statistics and probability can be introduced at the school and college stage in precisely the same way as the corresponding principles in mechanics are illustrated in the laboratory. It is hoped, therefore, shortly to supplement the present small volume by a manual of laboratory experiments on probability and statistics suitable for schools and colleges.

H. L.
E. E. P.

CONTENTS

ELEMENTARY STATISTICS

INTRODUCTION

STATISTICS used to be regarded as a very dull and dry subject, of interest only to a peculiar type of expert. By means of statistics, it was argued, one could prove anything. Nothing could indeed be further from the truth. Facts and figures are all we have on the basis of which we can rest our theories, and if our decisions are to be correct such a result can come only from a correct and just handling of the facts. Statistics is concerned precisely with this ; and because statisticians, when they have analysed their figures, do not differ among themselves seriously with regard to the conclusions that can be drawn, there is no ground whatsoever for the naïve statement that statistics can prove anything. One can always find faked evidence, or carefully doctored evidence, to make any case appear plausible. Statistics is concerned with undermining doctored evidence of this nature. It seeks to answer a very simply stated question, viz. Given certain facts and figures, what conclusions are we entitled to draw ?

In striving to answer this question, it raises another. By what methods can facts and figures be analysed so that as much as possible of the information they contain can be presented in a just way ? In this book we are concerned with some of these methods.

No educated person can afford to dispense with some knowledge of statistics. This may seem a very strange thing to say, since many so-called educated people appear to have no knowledge of the subject whatsoever ; but it is not difficult to see that such people in spite of their educational attainments are necessarily blind of an eye. Let us illustrate this.

We may say that 3 plus 2 are 5. We do not say that 3 plus 2 tend to be 5, or are roughly 5, or are sometimes 5. The statement is exact and precise ; but there are not really many statements in real life that are as simple as that.

Your height is 5' 10½". Your age is 26 years. You are 36" round the chest. Your friends are about 25 years of age. You have about 7 shillings in your pocket usually, you get 7 or 8 hours' sleep, you walk 10 miles per day, you smoke 12 cigarettes per day, and so on. Notice that to each of these statements one could have added the words " more or less," meaning that sometimes it is more, sometimes less, according to circumstances. Now these are all facts about real life, and yet they have not the terrifying precision of single numbers. If one always smoked 12 cigarettes each day exactly, always slept 7 hours exactly, always walked 10 miles each day exactly, always had 7 shillings exactly in one's pocket, remained exactly 5' 10½" in height, and 36" round the chest all day long whether one breathed or not, one would be a machine, not a human being. Statistics, therefore, is concerned with the idea of "more or less." So one must know how to talk about them intelligently, know what numbers mean when they are more, and what when they are less ; otherwise one cannot be an educated person because so much of one's ordinary life is linked up with such ideas.

But there is another side to this that is worth seeing. We are not always dealing with an isolated individual. We very often have to deal with groups : a squad of men, a regiment, or a battalion. Even when we deal with an individual, as we have seen, he is not always exactly the same. His chest measurement varies from time to time. So does the number of hours he sleeps or the amount of money he has in his pocket. In a sense he is a group of different people, and when we talk about him we are talking about the various kinds of people he is. Unless we realize that he does vary in this way we shall make the mistake of confusing him with a tailor's dummy.

We can carry it a stage further. Suppose he is in training as a marksman. It is no use saying simply that he gets one shot in five on the bull's eye, and leaving it like that. Sometimes he gets one in four and sometimes he does so badly that he gets only one in ten. If we say that on the average he succeeds once in five, will it be good enough to keep on taking his average to settle whether he is improving? He might have a very bad patch even while he is really improving. Moreover, how many shots should one take to settle his average at any stage? These are questions that a person educated or expert in this field ought to be able to answer. But a person, no matter how educated he is otherwise, will not be able to handle such questions unless he knows something about statistics.

And so we are irresistibly driven to the conclusion that just as we expect a normal person to know his multiplication table and his alphabet, to be able to read and write, so we expect a really educated person to be able to understand the meaning of figures and to be able to draw from them whatever information can be wrung out.

We may conclude with a reference to an advertisement issued by a certain society which has put up posters dealing with immunization against diphtheria. These state, quite baldly, that during the 30 months ending June 1942 approximately 5,000 cases of diphtheria occurred among immunized children. One is expected to infer that immunization has proved a failure. It is true that during the period in question 5,235 immunized children suffered from diphtheria, but it is also true that during the same period 75,974 unimmunized children also got diphtheria.

To make an accurate comparison one must know the proportion of children immunized, but these are not available. We have accurate statistics for the year 1942. These show that unimmunized children are nearly six times as likely to contract diphtheria as those who have been immunized, and nearly thirty times as likely to die of it.

It is obvious that a bald statement of the figures indicated in the advertisement can only create a false effect if the public generally are uncritical in their acceptance of the meaning of the statistics presented to them.

We repeat—no educated person can afford to dispense with a knowledge of statistics.

CHAPTER I

TYPES OF MEASUREMENT

In this book we are proposing to deal with sets of numbers from which information has to be drawn. These numbers may be the results of actual experiments which have been set up and carefully planned. In that case, if the experiment is well conducted, they will represent fairly accurate measurements. On the other hand, they may not represent experiments conducted by anyone, but material which has been collected together without exercising any control over what is happening. They might, for example, be figures giving the number of cars which pass a given point in the road during successive intervals of one minute, or they might be records of the temperature of the room taken every half hour, or every hour throughout the day and night. Let us mention a number of illustrations of both types.

First type

1. The number of hours a particular engine will run on ten gallons of petrol.
2. The force that has to be applied to an iron wire of circular cross section, $\frac{1}{16}''$ in diameter and $1'$ long, in order to make it extend $\frac{1}{16}''$, or $\frac{1}{8}''$, or $\frac{3}{16}''$.
3. The current that will circulate in a wire of given size and material when connected to the two poles of a battery whose voltage difference is one volt, or two volts, or three volts.
4. The time taken for a pendulum $1'$ in length to make a complete swing.

Second type

5. The number of visitors entering a museum per day.
6. The number of accidents per week in a factory.

7. The number of screws per thousand manufactured that show the presence of some defect.

8. The number per thousand of recruits who wear glasses.

9. The proportion of soldiers in a section whose heights range between 5′ 9″ and 5′ 10″.

If the first four of these are examined it will be seen that in every case, if great care is taken with the actual experiments indicated, it should be possible so to perfect them as to obtain *very nearly* the same result in each case. This is the kind of thing one expects to find in a good experiment. Slight differences will, of course, occur, and we shall have something to say later of the nature of these differences and how they arise, but the fact does remain that for practical purposes it is possible to repeat or verify the results by taking proper precautions.

This is not true, however, of the second type.

The number of visitors who enter a museum is not influenced by those conducting the inquiry. They have no control over the situation ; their business is merely to register what occurs. On Tuesday they do not repeat the results obtained on Monday, and because they have no control over it they cannot attempt to repeat the experiment. Nevertheless, although there may be quite a considerable difference in the numbers who enter a museum from day to day, yet, as we shall see, the figures do give us information on the point about which we inquire, namely, how well the museum is attended.

The second example of the second type may give us a series of numbers that vary less widely than in the previous case, but even here there will be a variation from week to week. The same is true of the third example of the second type. A thousand screws may be turned out without a single one being defective, but there may be other batches of a thousand showing two, three, or ten defective screws. From the point of view of standardization of production it is important to know whether such variations in defective screws as occur are on the increase or not, in order that attention may be turned, when necessary, to tracking down the causes should they show signs of serious increase.

Contrasting these two classes of illustrations we say that the measures of the first type are controlled experimental measures, and in that sense tend to provide a *unique number* to express what is sought. In the second type we say the results obtained provide *statistics* of the particular quality under examination. A study of these numbers therefore would lead us to consider in the first case the problem of experimental error, and in the second case the nature of the deviations from some average or typical value.

This can be seen again by the two following particular illustrations :

(1) Seven different samples of ordinary soft paraffin were heated in a beaker until they reached melting point, and the temperature was measured in each case with the following results :

$$60° \text{ C.}, \quad 65° \text{ C.}, \quad 62° \text{ C.}, \quad 62° \text{ C.}, \quad 64° \text{ C.}, \quad 63° \text{ C.}, \quad 65° \text{ C.}$$

It is clear that we could say that the melting point of paraffin is about 63° C., and the differences which occur from one case to the other might be regarded as due to varying degrees of impurity in the sample, or slightly different conditions under which the experiment is performed.

(2) Twenty men between the ages of 24 and 26 were timed over a distance of 100 yd. with the following results (in seconds) :

$$11\tfrac{4}{5}, 12, 11\tfrac{3}{5}, 11\tfrac{1}{5}, 12\tfrac{3}{5}, 12\tfrac{1}{5}, 11\tfrac{4}{5}, 13\tfrac{1}{5}, 11\tfrac{1}{5}, 12\tfrac{2}{5}, 12, 12\tfrac{1}{5}, 13,$$
$$12\tfrac{2}{5}, 14\tfrac{1}{5}, 11\tfrac{3}{5}, 12, 11\tfrac{4}{5}, 12\tfrac{1}{5}, 12.$$

Here is a set of figures giving the running performance of a group of people of a certain age. There is no unique figure, nor can we say that any one of the runners failed to achieve the *true* time for this group owing to some error in judgment. It is simply a record of diverse performances that cluster round about a value of approximately 12 seconds.

Summing up, therefore, we suppose that in the first type of illustration there is a unique value, but we never get it. Any actual reading is subject to an *error*. If we insist on truth we must also allow for error. In the second type of illustration every value we get is true, because it is one more of the set of numbers giving us information about the group. If we say there is no unique value, then they are all true !

EXERCISES

State in the following cases whether there is a unique or " true " number, or a statistical group of numbers to provide the answer :

1. How many hairs grow on a square inch of the scalp ?

2. How many words are there on this page ?

3. How many words are there on a page of this book ?

4. How many matches are there in a newly purchased box of matches ?

5. How many shots do you require to kill a rabbit at 30 yd. ?

6. How many shots did you require to kill a rabbit at 30 yd. ?

7. How many cigarettes do you smoke per day ?

8. How many cigarettes did you smoke yesterday ?

9. Explain what is meant by a controlled experiment ; give two illustrations.

10. If you can only observe what is taking place but can in no way control it, what would you expect the nature of your data to be ? Give illustrations even in such a case, where the data would still give a " unique " number.

CHAPTER II

FREQUENCY

IF one is collecting data concerning a certain kind of occurrence, as we have seen, the numbers obtained may either always be the same—or practically the same—or they may vary, sometimes quite considerably. When the same number is repeated we usually say we are verifying the result, that is, we are checking up that no mistake or error has been made in the count or in the measurement. When the numbers are different from one occasion to the next, then, as we have seen, each count gives us additional information about the whole set. We get more data. Some of the numbers are of course repeated several times, that is to say, some numbers occur more frequently than others. We may find that one number may occur most frequently. A study of the frequency with which the various numbers occur is therefore one of the first steps in examining data. It is part of the analysis of data in very much the same way as a chemical analysis helps us to understand the properties of the substance analysed. The numbers as a whole form a complete group, and we look at the various individual numbers in the group to see how well or how frequently they are represented.

A Study of Frequency

A paragraph of a book was taken and the number of times each of the five letters A, E, I, O, U appeared was counted. Here are the results :

A	E	I	O	U
15	17	19	16	3

If along a horizontal line we place A, E, I, O, U, in succession we can erect at each position a perpendicular line whose length will measure the number of times or the *frequency* with which that letter occurs.

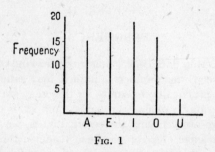

Fig. 1

This is simply a pictorial method of representing the table. There is no obvious connection between the succession of letters and the number of times each occurs.

Now let us consider a case in which there is a meaningful connection between the successive marks indicated on a horizontal line.

Of a group of 1,000 men on active duty, a number of men report sick each day. On certain days only 5, 7, or 10 report, although there may be an occasion when as many as 20 are sick. For the purposes of estimating the effective working capacity of the group it is important to know on any given day how many men may be expected to report as unwell. How are we to come to a reasonable estimate of this figure, if the numbers fluctuate from day to day in the way in which we have indicated? We could, of course, assert from a study of past records that there are always at least five, and that there have never been more than twenty (discounting special circumstances such as epidemics). The occurrence of only five, of course, is rare, so also is the occurrence of as many as twenty. On the other hand 8, 9, and 10 occur much more frequently. Suppose we examine the records over several weeks; we could then state what has actually occurred by means of a table of the following kind :

5 men reported sick on	1 occasion
6 ,, ,,	5 occasions
7 ,, ,,	11 ,,
8 ,, ,,	14 ,,
9 ,, ,,	16 ,,
10 ,, ,,	13 ,,
11 ,, ,,	10 ,,
12 ,, ,,	7 ,,
13 ,, ,,	4 ,,
15 ,, ,,	1 occasion
18 ,, ,,	1 ,,
20 ,, ,,	1 ,,

It is clear that the second column of figures, viz. 1, 5, 11, 14, 16, 13, 10, 7, 4, 1, 1, 1, can reasonably be called the frequency with which the number of illnesses indicated in the first column occur. All this can be simply set out in graphical form as follows. Vertically we plot the frequency and horizontally the number of cases having each of these frequencies. Thus in the present case we obtain the following picture :

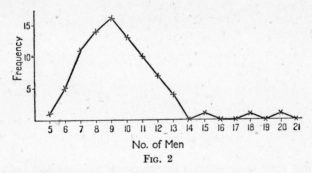

No. of Men

Fig. 2

The greatest number vertically is 16 which occurs when the number of men reported sick is 9. In this, 9 is called the *mode* as it is the value which occurs most frequently. The mode is not the most frequent number of times it occurs, but the quantity which occurs most frequently. If the points be joined the resulting figure is called a *frequency polygon*, or a *frequency curve* when a smooth curve is drawn through the points. In the present illustration, however, this has little meaning, because we cannot refer to the frequencies with which illnesses occur at any position other than whole numbers of men. This, however, is not always the case. Had the curve, for example, been one showing the lengths of time an aeroplane engine could run uninterruptedly until it broke down, there could have been times intermediate between the whole numbers placed along the horizontal axis whether these were hours or minutes. In such a case the horizontal line can refer to any interval of time over the whole range, and we can regard the quality referred to this line (in such a case, time) as varying continuously. The horizontal axis may describe a continuous or discontinuous characteristic. In practice, however, the distinction between these two is not as great as may at first sight appear. Let us illustrate this again.

Example : Let us suppose 100 men sprint 100 yd. and the time of each is noted. Here are the records of their performance :

$$2 \text{ men cover } 100 \text{ yd. in } 11\tfrac{1}{10} \text{ sec.}$$

4	,,	,,	$11\tfrac{1}{5}$	,,
8	,,	,,	$11\tfrac{2}{5}$	,,
14	,,	,,	$11\tfrac{3}{5}$	,,
23	,,	,,	$11\tfrac{4}{5}$	,,
34	,,	,,	12	,,
10	,,	,,	$12\tfrac{1}{5}$	,,
4	,,	,,	$12\tfrac{2}{5}$	,,
1 man covers		,,	$12\tfrac{3}{5}$	,,

Such a set of data could be represented graphically precisely as we have done with the cases of illness ; but we can examine them in a rather different way. If we group together the performances falling within ranges of a quarter of a second we have the following :

$$2+4 \qquad =6 \text{ men cover 100 yd. in } 11 \text{ to } 11\tfrac{1}{4} \text{ sec.}$$

8	,,	,,	$11\tfrac{1}{4}$,, $11\tfrac{1}{2}$	,,
14	,,	,,	$11\tfrac{1}{2}$,, $11\tfrac{3}{4}$	,,
$23+\tfrac{1}{2}(34) = 40$	,,	,,	$11\tfrac{3}{4}$,, 12	,,
$\tfrac{1}{2}(34)+10 = 27$	,,	,,	12 ,, $12\tfrac{1}{4}$	,,
4	,,	,,	$12\tfrac{1}{4}$,, $12\tfrac{1}{2}$.	,,
1 man covers	,,		$12\tfrac{1}{2}$,, $12\tfrac{3}{4}$	,,

A difficulty appears to arise at 12 sec., for those who have taken this time can be regarded as falling in the range $11\tfrac{3}{4}$ to 12 or 12 to $12\tfrac{1}{4}$. It is reasonable and customary to split the frequency between these groups ; thus in this case 17 are allotted to the group $11\tfrac{3}{4}$ to 12 and the same number to the group 12 to $12\tfrac{1}{4}$.

The frequency table can now be represented pictorially as follows :

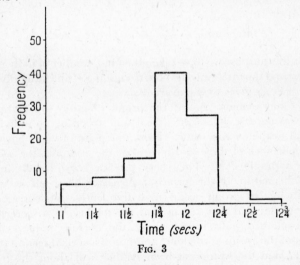

Fig. 3

Such a diagram is called a *histogram*.

In this case the mode corresponds to the range $11\tfrac{3}{4}$ to 12 sec. This means, in effect, that if these figures are typical of the performance of a group of such men and we have no further information concerning them, then our strongest expectation is that any given man will take between $11\frac{3}{4}$ and 12 sec. to cover the range. We can say, therefore, that this is the most " probable " time, based on past experience.

The mode as defined above is not always the same as the average (or the mean) time. This is clear if we calculate the average. Here is the actual calculation :

Total running time

$$= 2 \times 11\tfrac{1}{10} \quad + 4 \times 11\tfrac{1}{5} \quad + 8 \times 11\tfrac{2}{5} \quad + 14 \times 11\tfrac{3}{5} \quad + 23 \times 11\tfrac{4}{5}$$
$$\quad + 34 \times 12 \quad + 10 \times 12\tfrac{1}{5} \quad + 4 \times 12\tfrac{2}{5} \quad + 1 \times 12\tfrac{3}{5}$$
$$= 1184\tfrac{1}{5} \text{ sec.}$$

Total number of runners

$$= 2 + 4 + 8 + 14 + 23 + 34 + 10 + 4 + 1 = 100$$

$$\text{Average time} = \frac{1184 \cdot 2}{100} = 11 \cdot 84 \dots \text{sec.}$$

For this purpose we have taken the total number of individuals running and the total time devoted to running. The latter divided by the former gives us the average or *mean*.

We may remark that if the original figures are consulted there was no case where the actual time taken by an individual is equal to the average time. From our point of view, however, the importance of these two measures, the *mode* and the *average*, lies in a simple fact. They both provide us with information about the nature of the group *as a group*. They tell us which element in that group occurs most frequently (this corresponds to the mode) and they tell us that the totality, in a sense to be later examined, falls round about the average value. It is typical of the group as a whole, and not of a special section of the group. Had the histogram been symmetrical about the mode, that is to say, had corresponding vertical sections on each side of the mode at equal intervals from it been equal in height, giving a figure like this :

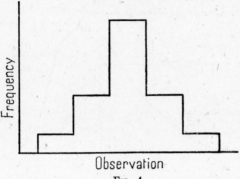

Fig. 4

the average would, in fact, have fallen in the centre of the modal range ; thus the difference between the average and the mode is an indication of the fact that the histogram is " lop-sided," or *skew* as it is called.

If the total number of observations can be increased indefinitely so that the class interval can be correspondingly decreased, the histogram gradually transforms into a frequency curve as the limiting case. The symmetry or otherwise of the histogram then

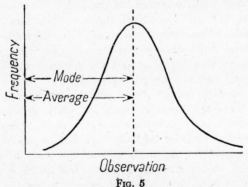

Fig. 5

Symmetrical Frequency Curve

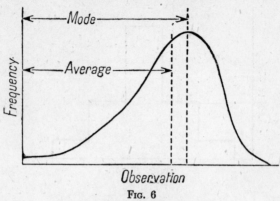

FIG. 6

Skew or Lop-sided Frequency Curve

shows itself in the symmetry or skewness of the frequency curve. (See Figs. 5 and 6.)

So far, it should be noticed, there is no special reason why we should have chosen the *average* to represent this group as a whole. It certainly provides a central value about which the other numbers fall, but we might have chosen a central value by taking the middle value, *i.e.* the time taken by, say, the 50th runner starting from either end of the table. This would have given $11\frac{1}{5}$ or $11\cdot8$ sec.—not very different from the average. Such a value is sometimes taken, and is called the *median*. It is clear that if the frequency polygon or the histogram were symmetrical, so that the *mode* and the *average* occurred at the same place, the *median* would also occur there.

For the moment we choose to confine our attention to the average as the single value to typify the whole group, because we shall find it is more convenient and is more easily interpreted. We must beware, however, of imagining that the average represents the *true* value of the group. It is taken only as a typical value. Every actual reading is true. The average may not coincide with any of these. In that sense it is untrue, but that does not prevent it from being *typical* of the set.

EXERCISES

1. Ten people were asked to measure the length (in inches) of a certain line. Here are the results they obtained :

4·9, 4·7, 4·8, 4·6, 4·7, 4·8, 4·7, 4·6, 4·5, 4·7.

Find the average of these measurements, then group them together in the form of a frequency table, and draw the frequency polygon.

2. The numbers of fully formed tomatoes on 100 plants were counted, with the following results :

2 plants had	0	tomatoes
5 ,,	1	tomato
7 ,,	2	tomatoes
11 ,,	3	,,
18 ,,	4	,,
24 ,,	5	,,
12 ,,	6	,,
8 ,,	7	,,
6 ,,	8	,,
4 ,,	9	,,
3 ,,	10	,,

(i) How many tomatoes were there in all ?

(ii) What was the average number of tomatoes per plant ?

(iii) What was the mode or modal number of tomatoes ?

Draw the corresponding histogram.

3. A firm employs 84 men, whose wages per hr. are given below :

Wages per hr.	9d.	1/-	1/3	1/6	1/9	2/-	2/3
Nos. of men earning wages	4	12	17	20	15	10	6

Find the mean wage and draw the histogram and the frequency polygon.

4. Draw the frequency polygon corresponding to the following set of estimates of a weight (w) in grammes. f is the frequency of each measurement. Find the mean.

w.	·410	·411	·412	·413	·414	·415	·416	·417	·418
f.	1	3	8	18	19	17	7	2	1

5. Find the mean of 50 estimates of the length of a line in cm.

Length	10·0	10·1	10·2	10·3	10·4
f.	5	15	13	11	6

6. One hundred and forty-five observations were made on the number of bones in small animals with the following results :

No. of bones	41	42	43	44	45	46	47	51
Frequency	1	7	19	48	42	20	7	1

Find the mean number of bones.

CHAPTER III

" BEST " VALUE FOR A SET OF MEASUREMENTS

IF an individual sets out to measure the wing-span of an aeroplane he will find that on successive attempts his measurements will not be exactly the same. They may differ very slightly from one another. For a variety of reasons which are not difficult to set out it is unlikely that he will repeat the same measurement exactly. This becomes even more obvious when a group of people independently measure the wing-span of the same aeroplane. They may differ from each other in their judgment of what is to be regarded as the two tips, or in the precision with which they adjust their measuring instruments between successive steps in the process.

The final outcome is to provide a set of numbers differing among themselves. These, between them, represent the wing-span. We are entitled to ask what is the best length to take when no further information is provided which tells us that any one of these measurements is better or more reliable than any other. We assume that there is such a best length.

A similar situation, although at first sight it looks rather different, arises when we consider such a problem as the determination of the length of life of an electric lamp. A series of lamps all apparently identical are switched on, and a record kept of the number of hours each lamp burns before failure occurs. At first sight it would seem that there is no " best " length of life of a lamp. The lamps are in fact all different in this respect. On the other hand, on matters of illumination design and generally on problems relating to the use of such lamps, some figure is necessary to represent the time the lamp will last before it fuses. The distinction between this and the previous case seems to arise at first sight from the fact that we are inclined to say that the *best* number we derive from the measurements of wing-span is *actually* the length of the wing-span, whereas in this case the best number we derive for the duration of life of a lamp is not *necessarily* that of any lamp at all. We are not now concerned with this kind of distinction. The best value is that which has to be associated with a span of a wing or with the lamp for the purposes for which the wing-span or the lamp is used. In this sense there is no difference between the two. If we were to take the heights of all the men in a particular platoon there would be in the same way a best height which would be a measure of the normal height of a member of the platoon. The measurements of the duration of life of the lamps would provide us with a best value for the normal lamp.

How is this best value to be derived ? Again we can give a picture of the situation in this way. The following are twenty measurements obtained for the wing-span of an aeroplane by twenty different people : 39′ 8″, 39′ 9½″, 39′ 9″, 39′ 1½″, 39′ 11½″, 39′ 9″, 39′ 10″, 39′ 4″, 39′ 7″, 40′ 0″, 39′ 9″, 39′ 10″, 39′ 8½″, 39′ 11″, 39′ 6″, 39′ 9″, 39′ 8″, 39′ 7″, 39′ 9″, 39′ 10″.

In Fig. 7 the horizontal line is marked 1 to 20, corresponding to each individual measurement. Vertically above each number a point is placed at a height corresponding to the amount of

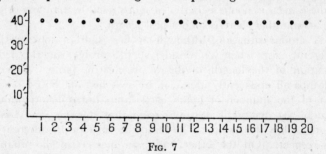

Fig. 7

the measurement. It is obvious how close these numbers lie to the same horizontal line. If we draw such a line to lie " evenly " among the points we can hardly distinguish on this diagram between one which lies at 39′ 4″ and 39′ 10″. This is because 39′ is a very large distance compared with 6″, the difference between these two measurements. To examine this more in detail it is better to use a larger scale which will emphasize the differences between the individual observations. This is done in Fig. 8, where only the region between 39′ and 40′ is mapped on

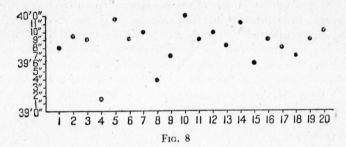

FIG. 8

the diagram. We are now faced, therefore, with the question : Where shall we decide to draw the horizontal line which would be most truly representative of the set of points as a whole ? A line which lies evenly among them will throw certain of the points above and the remainder below. The difference between an actual reading and this " best " value, called the *deviation*, will therefore be positive for points above the line and negative for points below. If the points actually lie on the line, the sum total of these deviations will be zero, since each is individually zero. Let us begin, therefore, by choosing the " best " value as such that the sum total of the deviations is zero, where of course some deviations are positive and some negative. This would be a reasonable method of approach. If we add up all the observations, then the sum total of the 20 will be 20 times the best value, plus the sum of the 20 deviations, some positive and some negative. The latter we say are to cancel out. Thus, the sum of the observations on this basis is 20 times the best value, which means in effect that the best value on this definition is the average value.

The average or mean value for a set of readings is that number which is such that the sum of the deviations of the observations from it is zero.

Exercise 1 : Work out the average of the following set of numbers, and verify that the sum of the deviations of these numbers from this average is zero : 1, 2, 3, 4, 5, 6, 7, 8, 9, 10, 11.

In practice it is usually convenient, in working out the average, to remember that the calculation of the result in this case is not affected if from each reading we take away a fixed amount, provided after we have found the average of the remainder we add this number back again. For example, in the case we have just considered we can take from each reading, such as 39′ 7″, the greater part of this, say 39′, so that we merely find the average of the remainders, namely :

No. of Reading	1	2	3	4	5	6	7	8	9	10
Remainder (in inches) after subtracting 39′	8	$9\frac{1}{2}$	9	$1\frac{1}{2}$	$11\frac{1}{2}$	9	10	4	7	12

No. of Reading	11	12	13	14	15	16	17	18	19	20
Remainder	9	10	$8\frac{1}{2}$	11	6	9	8	7	9	10

$$\text{Sum of remainders} = 169 \text{ in.}$$
$$\text{Average of remainders} = \frac{169 \text{ in.}}{20}$$
$$= 8 \cdot 45 \text{ in.}$$

This partial average must then be added to 39′ to give the true average, which is, therefore, 39′ 8·45″. It is obvious that in many cases this simple step will save an enormous amount of labour and therefore help to avoid the possibility of mistakes.

Exercise 2 : Find the average of the following six times :

1 min. 2 sec., 1 min., 64 sec., 59 sec., 54 sec., 1 min. 1 sec.

In the case with which we have just dealt, practically no measures were repeated, but, as is shown in our discussion in the last chapter on frequency diagrams, it is a very common thing for certain of the numbers to appear many times in the total set. This usually arises because the interval allows for the possibility of a number of measurements to fall within its range. In obtaining the average in such cases we must therefore be warned of a serious error into which it is easy to fall. The list of numbers in the frequency column really tells us, in each case, how often a number occurring in the previous column appears. To obtain the average, therefore, we must multiply each reading or measurement by the corresponding number in the frequency column, and after adding these the result must be divided by the total number of cases which occur, namely, the sum of the numbers occurring in the frequency column. It would be false to divide merely by the number of *different* readings.

Example : To find the mean directly.

The death rates per 1,000 from phthisis (consumption of the lungs) for London (1881–1900) are as follows. Find the mean age of death from phthisis :

Age (years)	15–25	25–35	35–45	45–55	55–65	65–75	75–85
Death rate per 1,000	343	380	530	547	464	271	114

In this example the *class limits* are 15, 25, 35 years, etc.; the *class interval* is 10 years ; the *central values* are 20, 30, 40 years, etc. The computation is best set out in columns, not rows, as follows :

Age (years) Central Values	Death rates per 1,000 *i.e.* Frequency of death	Age × Frequency
20	343	6860 = 20 × 343
30	380	11400 = 30 × 380
40	530	21200 = 40 × 530
50	547	27350 = 50 × 547
60	464	27840 = 60 × 464
70	271	18970 = 70 × 271
80	114	9120 = 80 × 114
	2649	122740

Thus the mean age of death from phthisis for London is

$$\frac{122740}{2649}$$

$$=46{\cdot}3 \text{ years}$$

In an earlier example we found the mean by subtracting a
" round " number from each observation and finding the partial
average of the remainders. We can choose any number (often
called a *fictitious average*) to subtract from each observation, but
if we choose a number within the range of observations, some
deviations will be positive and some negative.

The above example is worked through below, taking 40 years
as the fictitious average.

Example : Short method for finding the mean, taking 40 years
as fictitious average.

Age	Frequency	Deviation from 40	Deviation × Frequency
20	343	— 20	— 6860
30	380	— 10	— 3800
40	530	0	0
50	547	+ 10	+ 5470
60	464	+ 20	+ 9280
70	271	+ 30	+ 8130
80	114	+ 40	+ 4560
	2649		+ 27440
			— 10660
			+ 16780

The column (deviation × frequency) gives the total deviation
from the fictitious average 40.

Therefore the true mean differs from the fictitious mean by

$$+ \tfrac{16780}{2649} = + 6 \cdot 3 \text{ years}$$
$$\textit{i.e.} \text{ mean} = 40 + 6 \cdot 3 \text{ years}$$
$$= 46 \cdot 3 \text{ years.}$$

This method is independent of the number chosen as the fictitious average. The computation may also be further shortened by writing the deviations in class intervals.

For instance, considering the same example, take now the fictitious average to be 50 years, and notice that the class interval is 10 years.

Age	Frequency	Deviation from 50	Deviation in Class intervals	Deviation × Frequency
20	343	− 30	− 3	− 1029
30	380	− 20	− 2	− 760
40	530	− 10	− 1	− 530
50	547	0		0
60	464	+ 10	+ 1	+ 464
70	271	+ 20	+ 2	+ 542
80	114	+ 30	+ 3	+ 342
	2649			− 2319
				+ 1348
				− 971

i.e. the true mean differs from the fictitious mean by an

amount $= \dfrac{-971}{2649}$ class intervals

$= -0 \cdot 37$ class intervals

$= -3 \cdot 7$ years.   (Since 1 class interval is 10 years.)

∴ Mean $= 50 - 3 \cdot 7$

$= 46 \cdot 3$ years.

The histogram, frequency polygon, and true mean for this example are shown in the diagram below.

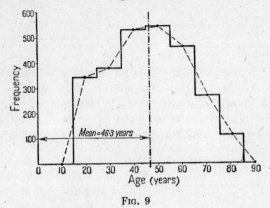

FIG. 9

The theoretical justification for the short method for finding the mean is as follows :

Suppose the fictitious mean is A, then the working in the general case would be

Observations	Frequency	Deviation from A	Frequency $\times$ Deviation
x_1	f_1	$x_1 - A$	$f_1(x_1 - A)$
x_2	f_2	$x_2 - A$	$f_2(x_2 - A)$
x_3	f_3	$x_3 - A$	$f_3(x_3 - A)$
.	.	.	.
.	.	.	.
.	.	.	.
x_n	f_n	$x_n - A$	$f_n(x_n - A)$

The sum of the column, frequency $\times$ deviation, divided by the total number of observations

$$= \frac{f_1(x_1 - A) + f_2(x_2 - A) + \ldots + f_n(x_n - A)}{f_1 + f_2 + \ldots + f_n}$$

$$= \frac{f_1 x_1 + f_2 x_2 + \ldots + f_n x_n}{f_1 + f_2 + \ldots + f_n} - A$$

$= M - A$

$=$ difference between true and fictitious means.

EXERCISES

1. A group of 40 people are tested for the length of time they can hold their breath, with the following results :

Time (sec.)	58	61	65	67	68	70	72
No. of Individuals	8	5	12	5	4	3	3

Find the average time by using the short method.

2. Two vertical lines are drawn close together on a vertical board and 20 individuals step back from it until they can no longer see the two lines as distinct. Here are the distances from the board at which this occurs :

Distance	21′ 6″	21′ 8″	21′ 10″	22′	22′ 2″
No. of Individuals	4	5	6	3	2

Use the short method to find the average distance.

3. Find the mean of the following measurements of a line in inches, using the long and short methods. Notice the saving of time in the latter case.

Length	8·60	8·59	8·58	8·57	8·56	8·55	8·54	8·53	8·52
Frequency	2	3	4	9	10	8	4	1	1

4. One hundred and twenty individuals firing at a moving target miss by the following distances, the positive and the negative signs corresponding to the shot being in advance or behind the target :-

1 shot is between	$+ 10$ and $+ 15$ in. wide		
3 shots are ,,	$+ 5$,, $+ 10$	,,
20 ,, ,,	0 ,, $+ 5$	,,
25 ,, ,,	$- 5$,, 0	,,
22 ,, ,,	$- 10$,, $- 5$	,,
17 ,, ,,	$- 15$,, $- 10$	,,
13 ,, ,,	$- 20$,, $- 15$	,,
10 ,, ,,	$- 25$,, $- 20$	,,
7 ,, ,,	$- 30$,, $- 25$	,,
2 ,, ,,	$- 35$,, $- 30$	,,

(i) Draw the corresponding histogram.

(ii) Find the average distance behind the target by which the shots tend to miss.

(iii) What proportion of the shots fall within a range of 5 in. either way of the target?

(iv) If shots that fall more than 10 in. wide of the target are classed as bad, what percentage of the shots are bad?

(v) Which stretch of 15 in. contains the greatest number of shots, and what fraction of the total shots falls inside this stretch?

5. From the collection of numbers 2, 4, 6, 8, 10, 12, all possible pairs of numbers are taken, and the average of each pair is found. Write down all these averages and the frequency with which each occurs.

Show that the average of this new collection of averages is the same as that of the original numbers, viz. 7.

Repeat this for all possible sets of three numbers obtained from the original set.

6. The monthly profits of 100 shops are distributed as follows :

Profit per shop (£)	0–10	10–20	20–30	30–40	40–50	50–60
No. of shops	12	18	27	20	17	6

Find the mean and draw the histogram.

7. The following table gives the lengths of 800 corn cobs in inches :

Length	5	5·5	6	6·5	7	7·5	8	8·5	9	9·5
Number	10	33	70	110	176	172	124	61	32	12

Determine the mean and draw the frequency polygon.

CHAPTER IV

HOW TO MEASURE DISPERSION

In the last chapter we were searching for a number which could be said to represent in the best way a given collection of numbers varying among themselves, and we came to the not unexpected conclusion that the average or mean satisfied this requirement. Now it is clear also that such a number represents the collection only in a very restricted sense. If, for example, we take the average of 99·9, 100·0, 100·1, we find it is 100. If, however, we took the numbers 0·1, 100·0, 199·9, once again we have the same average, namely, 100, but the two sets of numbers are very different. In the first case they are packed close to the average, in the second case they are widely spaced out. We must clearly have some additional measure which expresses for us *the extent of this " scattering " of the numbers about the average*, a number which, when it is small, will tell us that they are closely packed, and which, when it is large, will say that they are not. What we want, therefore, is some estimate of the size of the deviation of a typical or standard reading from the mean. Now for this purpose it is no use taking the average of the deviations themselves to find a typical size of deviation, for the simple reason that the sum of the deviations is zero. We have somehow or other to remove the effect of the differences in sign among the deviations. A convenient method of doing this is to take the squares of the deviations, for all squares are necessarily positive, and to find their average value. This will give us the average value of the squares of the deviations. But it is not the average of the squares we want, but some measure of the deviations themselves, so we take the square root of this quantity. This number is called the *Standard Deviation*. Let us define it in words. *The Standard Deviation is the square root of the average value of the squares of the deviations from the mean of the original readings.*

Let us work this out for the two simple cases we have just constructed.

1ST CASE			2ND CASE		
Numbers	Deviations from 100	(Deviations)²	Numbers	Deviations from 100	(Deviations)²
99·9	−0·1	+0·01	0·1	−99·9	9980·01
100·0	0	0	100·0	0	0
100·1	0·1	+0·01	199·9	99·9	9980·01
300·0	0·0	0·02	300·0	0·0	19960·02

Average $= \frac{300}{3} = 100$
Standard Deviation
$$= \sqrt{\frac{0·02}{3}}$$
$$= 0·082$$

Average $= \frac{300}{3} = 100$
Standard Deviation
$$= \sqrt{\frac{19960·02}{3}}$$
$$= 81·568$$

We notice, therefore, that while the two sets had the same average, the fact that they are very differently distributed about this average is brought out by the fact that the Standard Deviation in the one case is 0·082 and in the other 81·568.

Note : It is customary to write the standard deviation as σ (the Greek letter sigma).

If we use the notation of the previous chapter where x_1, x_2, . . . x_n are a set of n readings whose average is M, then

$$\sigma = \sqrt{\left[\frac{1}{n} \Big\{ (x_1 - M)^2 + (x_2 - M)^2 + \ldots + (x_n - M)^2 \Big\} \right]}$$

Furthermore, as in the treatment of averages, we have to remember that a table of values is usually a frequency table, that is, some of the items are repeated. In that case we have to follow the same procedure as we did in the case of averages, and multiply the square of each deviation by the frequency with which it occurs, dividing the result, of course, by the sum of the frequencies, and obtaining the standard deviation by taking the square root of this result. In terms of our notation, if $f_1, f_2, \ldots f_n$ are the frequencies with which the observations $x_1, x_2, \ldots x_n$ occur, then

$$\sigma = \sqrt{\left[\frac{f_1(x_1 - M)^2 + f_2(x_2 - M)^2 + \ldots + f_n(x_n - M)^2}{f_1 + f_2 + \ldots + f_n}\right]}$$

It should be noticed that in this case, although there are n *different* observations, the total number of observations is $f_1 + f_2 + \ldots + f_n$, because the observation x_1 is repeated f_1 times, x_2 is repeated f_2 times, and so on.

Example : Using the example of last chapter, to find the standard deviation.

Age	Frequency	Deviation from mean	(Deviation)^2	Frequency × (Deviation)^2
20	343	− 26·3	691·69	237249·67
30	380	− 16·3	265·69	100962·20
40	530	− 6·3	39·69	21035·70
50	547	+ 3·7	13·69	7488·43
60	464	+ 13·7	187·69	87088·16
70	271	+ 23·7	561·69	152217·99
80	114	+ 33·7	1135·69	129468·66
	2649			735510·81

Average or mean = 46·3 years

$$\text{Standard deviation} = \sqrt{\frac{735510 \cdot 81}{2649}}$$

$$= \sqrt{277 \cdot 656}$$

$$= 16 \cdot 66 \text{ years}$$

Short Method for calculating Standard Deviation

It will be seen from the foregoing example that although the numbers originally occurring were themselves whole numbers the mean involves the calculation in a series of decimals, so that the deviations and the calculation of their squares is often tedious. It is possible to shorten this calculation considerably by a simple device. We begin by taking a fictitious mean " A " and carrying through the calculation for the corresponding fictitious standard deviation as if for the standard deviation. We shall let s denote this fictitious standard deviation.

Then

$$s^2 = \frac{f_1(x_1 - A)^2 + f_2(x_2 - A)^2 + \ldots + f_n(x_n - A)^2}{f_1 + f_2 + \ldots + f_n}$$

Since by definition

$$\sigma^2 = \frac{f_1(x_1 - M)^2 + f_2(x_2 - M)^2 + \ldots + f_n(x_n - M)^2}{f_1 + f_2 + \ldots + f_n}$$

therefore

$$(f_1 + f_2 + \ldots + f_n)(s^2 - \sigma^2) = 2(M - A)(f_1 x_1 + f_2 x_2 + \ldots f_n x_n) + (A^2 - M^2)(f_1 + f_2 + \ldots + f_n).$$

Thus

$$
\begin{aligned}
s^2 - \sigma^2 &= 2(M - A)\left(\frac{f_1 x_1 + f_2 x_2 + \ldots + f_n x_n}{f_1 + f_2 + \ldots + f_n}\right) + A^2 - M^2 \\
&= 2(M - A)M + A^2 - M^2 \\
&= M^2 - 2AM + A^2 \\
&= (M - A)^2 \\
\text{or} \quad \sigma^2 &= s^2 - (M - A)^2
\end{aligned}
$$

We shall now apply this device to our previous example, and further shorten the labour by working in class intervals.

Example : To find the standard deviation in the previous example by the short method.

Take the fictitious mean (A) to be 50 years. The class interval is 10 years.

Age	Frequency	Deviation from 50	Deviation in class intervals	(Deviation)^2	(Deviation)^2 × Frequency
20	343	− 30	− 3	9	3087
30	380	− 20	− 2	4	1520
40	530	− 10	− 1	1	530
50	547	0	0	0	0
60	464	10	1	1	464
70	271	20	2	4	1084
80	114	30	3	9	1026
	2649				7711

Therefore $s^2 = \frac{7711}{2649} = 2\cdot911$ in class intervals.

Also $M - A$ (the difference between the true mean and the fictitious mean) was found in the last chapter to equal $-0\cdot37$ class intervals. Hence

$$\sigma^2 = s^2 - (M - A)^2$$
$$= 2\cdot911 - (-0\cdot37)^2$$
$$= 2\cdot774$$
$$\therefore \quad \sigma = 1\cdot666 \text{ class intervals}$$
$$= 16\cdot66 \text{ years, which agrees with the result previously obtained.}$$

It should be self-evident that the units in which the mean and the standard deviation are expressed are the same as that in the original readings. If a series of measurements of a length are in feet, then the average is also expressed in feet, and so also is the standard deviation.

EXERCISES

1. Find the standard deviation of the following sets of numbers without using the short method :

   (i) 1, 2, 3.   (ii) 1, 2, 3, 4, 5.   (iii) 1, 2, 3, 4, 5, 6, 7.

2. (More difficult mathematically)   Find the standard deviation of the set of $2n-1$ numbers :

$$1, 2, 3, 4, 5, \ldots (2n - 2), (2n - 1).$$

3. Use the short method for finding the standard deviation of the following sets of numbers :

$\quad$(i) 1, 2. $\quad$(ii) 1, 2, 3, 4. $\quad$(iii) 1, 2, 3, 4, 5, 6.

4. (More difficult mathematically.) Find the standard deviation of the set of $2n$ numbers :

$$1, 2, 3, 4, \ldots (2n - 1), \ 2n.$$

5. If in calculating the standard deviation, the sum of the squares of the actual observations has been taken by mistake instead of the sum of the squares of the deviations from the mean, show that the true standard deviation can be obtained by reducing the square of the erroneous standard deviation by the square of the mean and extracting the square root.

6. Ten measurements (in feet) were made with the following results. Find the mean and the standard deviation.

$\quad$Length (ft.) $\quad$ 77, 73, 75, 70, 72, 76, 75, 71, 74, 78.

7. The mean daily sunshine for Great Britain and Ireland for the years 1881–1915 is given below :

	Jan.	Feb.	Mar.	Apl.	May	June	July	Aug.	Sep.	Oct.	Nov.	Dec.
hr.	1·42	2·40	3·63	5·19	6·18	6·26	5·68	5·19	4·47	2·99	1·86	1·16

Find the average number of hours' sunshine per day and the standard deviation.

8. Plot the histogram of the following distribution, and find the mean and the standard deviation :

Observation: central values (cm.)	0·80	0·85	0·90	0·95	1·00	1·05	1·10	1·15	1·20	1·25
Frequency	4	14	28	32	14	14	5	3	2	1

9. Find the standard deviation in the case of the following 40 measurements of x :

x	16	17	18	19	20	21	22
Frequency	2	5	8	10	9	5	1

10. The standard deviations of two sets, each of n numbers, are σ_1 and σ_2, measured from their respective means M_1 and M_2. The two sets are then grouped together as one set of $2n$ numbers ; show that the standard deviation σ of this set, measured from its new mean, is given by

$$\sigma^2 = \tfrac{1}{2}\,(\sigma_1{}^2 + \sigma_2{}^2) + \tfrac{1}{4}\,(M_1 - M_2)^2$$

CHAPTER V

SPECIAL TYPES OF FREQUENCY

THE scattering of a set of measures shows itself not only in the range over which the readings spread, but in the heaping-up of the observations and the variation of this heaping-up from one part of the range to the next. This has already been seen when we have considered frequency curves ; and the precise way in which this frequency affects the value of the standard deviation has been examined. Here, therefore, we propose to look a little more closely at certain special kinds of frequency and how they are built up.

(A) THE FREQUENCY OF THE AVERAGE

Suppose we have the series of numbers

$$2, 4, 6, 8, 10,$$

each of which occurs once. Their average is, of course, 6. Suppose we make trial samples of this " population " by selecting two of these each time and taking their average. If we take every possible pair of two, what set of averages will we obtain ? Let us write down all the possible pairs, and the average of each pair, like this :

Sample	Aver.	Sample	Aver.	Sample	Aver.
2, 4	3	4, 6	5	6, 8	7
2, 6	4	4, 8	6	6, 10	8
2, 8	5	4, 10	7	8, 10	9
2, 10	6				

Thus we have the following frequency table :

Average	3	4	5	6	7	8	9
Frequency	1	1	2	2	2	1	1

Exercise 1 : Check that the average of this set is again 6, the same as that of the original population.

These new numbers, therefore, are grouped around the same average, but the numbers in the neighbourhood of the average are more heavily weighted. The frequency curve which for the original set of numbers was simply a horizontal line, since each number appeared once only, has now developed a hump in it around the average. Let us carry this step one stage further. We take the ten numbers in this table and select all possible samples of two numbers, working out the average in each case like this :

Series of numbers

3, 4, 5, 5, 6, 6, 7, 7, 8, 9.

Sample	Aver.	Sample	Aver.	Sample	Aver.	Sample	Aver.	Sample	Aver.
3, 4	3·5	4, 5	4·5	5, 6	5·5	5, 7	6	6, 7	6·5
3, 5	4	4, 5	4·5	5, 6	5·5	5, 8	6·5	6, 8	7
3, 5	4	4, 6	5	5, 7	6	5, 9	7	6, 9	7·5
3, 6	4·5	4, 6	5	5, 7	6	6, 6	6	7, 7	7
3, 6	4·5	4, 7	5·5	5, 8	6·5	6, 7	6·5	7, 8	7·5
3, 7	5	4, 7	5·5	5, 9	7	6, 7	6·5	7, 9	8
3, 7	5	4, 8	6	5, 6	5·5	6, 8	7	7, 8	7·5
3, 8	5·5	4, 9	6·5	5, 6	5·5	6, 9	7·5	7, 9	8
3, 9	6	5, 5	5	5, 7	6	6, 7	6·5	8, 9	8·5

We can write this now more compactly as follows :

Average	3·5	4	4·5	5	5·5	6	6·5	7·	7·5	8	8·5
Frequency	1	2	4	5	7	7	7	5	4	2	1

Exercise 2 : Check that the average of this set is again 6.

Again we see that the numbers are grouped around the same average, and again the numbers in the neighbourhood of the average are more heavily weighted. Moreover, at each successive stage the range has shrunk. It began with a range 2—10. It became 3—9, and finally 3·5—8·5. For these reasons we must expect also that the standard deviation of the averages will be less than that of the original set of numbers.

Exercise 3 : Find the mean and the standard deviation of the numbers 3, 5, 7, 9, 11, 13.

Show that if all possible pairs of these numbers are taken, and the average of each pair is calculated, the mean of this new set is the same as that of the original, but its standard deviation is about 0·7 of the original.

We shall show shortly that in general the accuracy of the average, as compared with the accuracy of any one of the n readings used to form the average, increases as $\sqrt{n}$. Stated otherwise, we shall show that the standard deviation falls off as $\sqrt{n}$.

(B) Frequency Table obtained by Coin-Tossing

If we imagine a perfectly balanced coin, with a head on one side and a tail on the other, we can say that if it is tossed " fairly," no bias can show itself. Such an idealized case, therefore, would indicate that if the coin were tossed twice, " no head " would appear once corresponding to the arrangement T, T, and one head would appear once, corresponding to the arrangement T, H, where T stands for tail, and H for head.

Now consider two coins tossed simultaneously. We could have the following arrangements :

$$T, T ; T, H ; H, T ; H, H.$$

Thus *no heads* occurs on 1 occasion
    one head occurs on 2 occasions
    two heads occurs on 1 occasion

This is shown in the histogram, Fig. 10.

Consider now three coins tossed simultaneously. We could have the following arrangements :

T, T, T ; T, T, H ; T, H, T ; H, T, T ; T, H, H ; H, T, H ;
H, H, T ; H, H, H.

Thus *no heads*   occurs on 1 occasion
     one head   occurs on 3 occasions
     two heads   occurs on 3 occasions
     three heads occurs on 1 occasion

This is shown in the histogram, Fig. 11.

If four coins were simultaneously tossed, it is not difficult to see that the following results would be obtained (Fig. 12) :

Number of Heads	0	1	2	3	4
Number of Occasions	1	4	6	4	1

If we look at the frequencies, viz. 1, 1 ; 1, 2, 1 ; 1, 3, 3, 1 ; 1, 4, 6, 4, 1, we notice that these require the coins to be tossed, 2, 4, 8, and 16 times, *i.e.* 2^1, 2^2, 2^3, 2^4 times respectively, in order that all the possible arrangements may be represented.

In order to link this special illustration with the more general case we propose to treat, let us restate each of these tossings in the form of a question whose answer is provided in the results we have found for the frequency.

Out of a collection of two coins, in how many ways can we draw a sample showing no head, or a sample showing one head, or two heads ? Out of a collection of three coins how many samples can be drawn showing no heads, one head, two heads, three heads ?

Out of a collection of four coins, in how many different ways can we find a sample showing a head, in how many ways can we find a sample showing two heads only, three heads only,

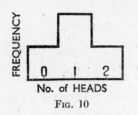

FREQUENCY

No. of HEADS

FIG. 10

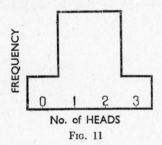

FREQUENCY

No. of HEADS

FIG. 11

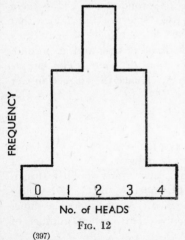

FREQUENCY

No. of HEADS

FIG. 12

or four heads? Now for our purpose the tails might as well have been non-existent. We were concerned only with the heads. Thus, although in the case of four coins we imagined we had drawn four coins on each occasion, the real number of coins with which we were concerned on each occasion was simply the number of heads that showed themselves in each batch. Thus, we might imagine we had N coins lying on the table, head upwards. We can then ask:

1. In how many ways can we select one coin?

2. In how many ways can we select two coins?

3. In how many ways can we select three coins? And so on.

It should be noticed that in this way we are examining all the possible types of occurrence that could take place, and how frequently each type could occur. Thus we are really studying random sampling from a collection of N objects. Let us examine this question, then, in a more general form.

4

(C) THE BINOMIAL DISTRIBUTION

Out of a given collection of N different objects, how many different samples can be drawn consisting of one object, or two objects, or three objects, and so on ?

If we can calculate these we may be able to obtain an estimate of the average size of a sample ; we should be able to draw a frequency curve showing the frequency with which samples of various sizes may be drawn, and we may be able to calculate the standard deviation for the sizes of such samples, giving us, therefore, a measure of the way in which samples crowd in around the average.

(i) *Sample of Size—1 Object*

It is obvious that for N different objects there are N different ways in which a sample of 1 object may be drawn.

(ii) *Sample of Size—2 Objects*

We can choose the first object in N ways, and for each of these there are N — 1 ways of choosing the second object. Thus there are N (N — 1) ways of choosing two objects. But notice that in this each sample is drawn twice. For instance, we may draw A first and B next, or we may draw B first and A second. We have counted these as if they were different. The sample A, B is the same as the sample B, A. Hence the correct answer is N(N — 1)/2.

(iii) *Sample of Size—3 Objects*

We may choose the first in N ways, the second in N — 1 ways, and the third in N — 2 ways. This would give N(N — 1)(N — 2) samples were it not for the fact that each group would be drawn six times by this method. For example, A, B, C ; A, C, B ; B, C, A ; B, A, C ; C, A, B ; C, B, A. All these are the same. Thus there are six times too many. The correct number of samples of three, therefore, is $N(N-1)(N-2)/6$ or, as we prefer to write it, $N(N-1)(N-2)/1 \times 2 \times 3$.

We prefer to write it in this way for a simple reason. It is clear that on each occasion we have to divide the successive product in the numerator by the number of ways in which the objects in the sample may be arranged among themselves. Thus :

(iv) *Sample of Size—4 Objects*

We shall have to divide $N(N-1)(N-2)(N-3)$ by the number of ways 4 objects may be arranged in all possible orders. Let us examine what this is. Imagine the 4 objects and suppose we are forming all the arrangements. We can choose the first in 4 ways, and having done so we choose the second in 3 ways. There are, therefore, 4×3 ways of choosing the first two. We can then choose the third in 2 ways, and the last in 1 way only. The total number of arrangements, therefore, of all four objects is $4 \times 3 \times 2 \times 1$. It is this number that has to divide $N(N-1)(N-2)(N-3)$. Thus there are $N(N-1) (N-2) (N-3)/1 \times 2 \times 3 \times 4$ samples of size 4 objects.

It is usual to write products like

1×2 as 2!	and read it " factorial 2 "	
$1 \times 2 \times 3$ as 3!	,,	,, 3
$1 \times 2 \times 3 \times 4$ as 4!	,,	,, 4

We thus have the following table :

Size of Sample	Number of Samples drawn from N objects
0	1
1	N
2	$N(N-1)/2!$
3	$N(N-1) (N-2)/3!$
4	$N(N-1) (N-2) (N-3)/4!$
5	$N(N-1) (N-2) (N-3) (N-4)/5!$
. . . . .	
r	$N(N-1)(N-2) \ldots (N-r+1)/r!$

The numbers on the right really give us the frequency with which samples of the sizes given on the left can be drawn.

Note : It is often convenient to write $N(N - 1) (N - 2) \ldots (N - r + 1)/r!$ in the equivalent form $N! (N - r)!/r!$

Example : If $N = 6$ we would have the following table :

Size of Sample	0	1	2	3	4	5	6
Frequency	1	6	15	20	15	6	1

Average size of sample :

$$= \frac{1 \times 0 + 6 \times 1 + 15 \times 2 + 20 \times 3 + 15 \times 4 + 6 \times 5 + 1 \times 6}{1 + 6 + 15 + 20 + 15 + 6 + 1}$$

$$= 192/64 = 3$$

Standard Deviation :

$$= \sqrt{\frac{(1 \times 9 + 6 \times 4 + 15 \times 1 + 20 \times 0 + 15 \times 1 + 6 \times 4 + 1 \times 9)}{64}}$$
$$= \sqrt{\tfrac{96}{64}} = \sqrt{\tfrac{3}{2}}$$

Note : Total number of samples in this case is $64 = 2^6$. In this case also we notice that the frequency curve will be symmetrical about the mean, since the values of the frequency are the same, running from left to right, as right to left.

It is not difficult to see that this must be true in general. For the number of ways of drawing a sample of size r is exactly the number of ways of leaving $N - r$ undrawn; but each time we leave $N - r$ undrawn we are in fact selecting these $N - r$ objects for the purpose of not drawing them. They are therefore a sample of $N - r$ objects. It follows that the number of samples of size r is equal to the number of samples of size $N - r$; consequently the frequency curve must be symmetrical about the central value, viz. $N/2$. Thus the average size of a sample is $N/2$.

How many possible samples are there altogether ?

To obtain this we have to add together all the items in the frequency column, viz :

$$1+N+\frac{N(N-1)}{2!}+\frac{N(N-1)(N-2)}{3!}+\ldots+\frac{N(N-1)\ldots(N-r+1)}{r!}$$
$$+\ldots+N+1$$

We can easily find a compact expression for this if we use the Binomial Theorem :

$$(1+x)^N = 1 + Nx + \frac{N(N-1)}{2!}x^2 + \frac{N(N-1)(N-2)}{3!}x^3$$
$$+\ldots+Nx^{N-1}+x^N$$

In this it will be noticed that the coefficients are exactly the terms in our frequency column. Hence by putting $x = 1$ in this expression, the expression on the left becomes $(1+1)^N = 2^N$, which is therefore the total number of samples that may be drawn.

Direct Calculation of the Mean

If we differentiate this binomial expression with respect to x, we find :

$$N(1+x)^{N-1} = N + \frac{N(N-1)}{2!}2x + \frac{N(N-1)(N-2)}{3!}3x^2 + \ldots + Nx^{N-1}$$

If now in this we replace x by 1, we obtain

$$N.2^{N-1} = N + \frac{N(N-1)}{2!}.2 + \frac{N(N-1)(N-2)}{3!}.3 + \ldots + 1.N$$

The expression on the right is the sum of each frequency multiplied by the size of the sample having that frequency in each case. Hence, if we divide it by the total number of samples, viz. 2^N, we obtain the mean or average size of a sample.

Thus, average size of a sample

$$= N2^{N-1}/2^N = N/2$$

as already found.

Direct Calculation of the Standard Deviation

Let us illustrate the method with the example corresponding to $N = 6$, for we have already calculated the standard deviation as $\sqrt{\frac{3}{2}}$.

We begin by writing the particular case of the Binomial Theorem :

$$(1 + x)^6 = 1 + 6x + 15x^2 + 20x^3 + 15x^4 + 6x^5 + x^6$$

Here the coefficients are the frequency values as tabulated in the example.

If we choose zero as a fictitious average instead of 3, as already found we have to calculate first the fictitious standard deviation. Each value of the frequency has to be multiplied by the *square* of the size of sample. We begin by differentiating :

Thus

$$6(1+x)^5 = 6 + 15 \times 2x + 20 \times 3x^2 + 15 \times 4x^3 + 6 \times 5x^4 + 1 \times 6x^5$$

Now multiply both sides by x and differentiate again.
The right-hand side becomes

$$6 + 15 \times 2^2 x + 20 \times 3^2 x^2 + 15 \times 4^2 x^3 + 6 \times 5^2 x^4 + 1 \times 6^2 x^5$$

while the left-hand side becomes the differential coefficient of

$$6x(1 + x)^5, \text{ i.e. } 6(1 + x)^5 + 30x (1 + x)^4$$

Now, inserting $x = 1$ in each of these and equating both sides we obtain :

$$6 \times 2^5 + 30 \times 2^4 = 6 + 15 \times 2^2 + 20 \times 3^2 + 15 \times 4^2$$
$$+ 6 \times 5^2 + 1 \times 6^2$$

If we divide this by the total number of samples, viz. 2^6, we get the square of the fictitious standard deviation, which is therefore $(6 \times 2^5 + 30 \times 2^4)/2^6 = \frac{6}{2} + \frac{30}{4}$
$$= \frac{21}{2}$$

Using the formula

$$\sigma^2 = s^2 - (M - A)^2$$

and noting that the mean is 3 and the fictitious mean is zero, we find

$$\sigma^2 = \frac{21}{2} - 9 = \frac{3}{2}$$
$$\sigma = \sqrt{\frac{3}{2}} \text{ as already found.}$$

Now consider the general case, using the same method. We write

$$(1 + x)^N = 1 + Nx + \frac{N(N-1)}{2!}x^2 + \frac{N(N-1)(N-2)}{3!}x^3 + \dots$$

Differentiating once we have

$$N(1 + x)^{N-1} = N + \frac{N(N-1)}{2!} \cdot 2x + \frac{N(N-1)(N-2)}{3!}3x^2 + \dots$$

If we multiply by x and differentiate again we get on the right

$$N + \frac{N(N-1)}{2!}2^2x + \frac{N(N-1)(N-2)}{3!}3^2x^2 + \dots$$

and on the left, the differential coefficient of $Nx(1 + x)^{N-1}$ is $N(1 + x)^{N-1} + N(N - 1)x(1 + x)^{N-1}$. Putting $x = 1$ on both sides, we find that

$$N + \frac{N(N-1)}{2!}2^2 + \frac{N(N-1)(N-2)}{3!}3^2 + \dots$$

$$= N \cdot 2^{N-1} + N(N - 1)2^{N-2}$$

The square of the fictitious standard deviation is the expression

on the left when divided by 2^N, the total number of samples.
Hence

$$s^2 = [N \cdot 2^{N-1} + N(N-1)2^{N-2}]/2^N$$
$$= N/2 + N(N-1)/4.$$

To obtain σ^2 we have to take away from s^2 the square of the mean value, *i.e.* $N^2/4$. Finally, therefore :

$$\sigma^2 = N/2 + N(N-1)/4 - N^2/4 = N/4$$
$$\text{or } \sigma = \tfrac{1}{2}\sqrt{N}$$

It is evident that when $N = 6$ this verifies the value already found.

EXERCISES

1. Two dice are marked with the numbers 1 to 6. Set down all the numbers that the sums of these faces may show when the dice are thrown, and the frequency with which each number occurs. Find the average sum obtained on throwing the dice.

2. Three bags contain respectively 10 red balls, 8 black balls, and 6 white balls. If samples of two are drawn always of two different colours, how many such samples are there altogether and what proportion of these will consist of black and white balls ?

3. Draw the frequency diagram corresponding to each row of binomial coefficients taken as frequencies, in each case finding the mean and the standard deviation :

x	0	1	2	3	4	5	6	7	8	9	10
f_1	1	1									
f_2	1	2	1								
f_3	1	3	3	1							
f_4	1	4	6	4	1						
f_5	1	5	10	10	5	1					
f_6	1	6	15	20	15	6	1				
f_7	1	7	21	35	35	21	7	1			
f_8	1	8	28	56	70	56	28	8	1		
f_9	1	9	36	84	126	126	84	36	9	1	
f_{10}	1	10	45	120	210	252	210	120	45	10	1

Note : Each of these binomial coefficients is the sum of the number just above it in the table and the number to the left of the latter.

4. Verify that in the last example the sum of the frequencies is in succession 2, 2^2, 2^3, 2^4, 2^5, 2^6, 2^7, 2^8, 2^9, 2^{10}. Explain why this is so.

5. Show that there are $N + 1$ terms in the binomial set, and that if N is even, the middle term is the $(1 + N/2)$th term, while if N is odd, the two equal middle terms are the $(N + 1)/2$th term and the $(N + 3)/2$th term. Write down the expression for this middle term for the case where N is even, and show that its value can be written $N!/\left(\dfrac{N}{2}!\right)^2$.

6. Show that the proportion of the total readings that occur at the mean position is $N!/2^N\left(\dfrac{N}{2}!\right)^2$.

7. Reconstruct the table in Exercise 3 so that each number shows the proportion of the total readings that occur at each value of x.

8. Reconstruct the table in Exercise 3 or that in Exercise 7 so that the frequency is replaced by the product of the standard deviation for the set into the proportion of the total readings that occur at that value of x.

9. Plot the result of Exercise 8 vertically against x horizontally.

10. Plot the result of Exercise 8 vertically against $x/\bar{x}$ horizontally where $\bar{x}$ is the mean value of x, viz. $N/2$.

Note : The curves obtained in Exercises 9 and 10 should be re-examined after reading Chapter XII, on Gauss's Law of Error.

CHAPTER VI

THE ACCURACY OF THE MEAN

A VERY practical problem that arises in the collection of data is to decide exactly how much data to collect. Broadly speaking we can say that this is usually settled by the amount of labour demanded in the collection and in the subsequent analysis. To carry on the collection beyond a certain stage may become quite prohibitive. Is it possible to arrive at some understanding of the gain in accuracy that accrues from doubling or trebling the number of observations? If we are taking measurements of what is presumed to be the same unique quantity, and if we are satisfied to take the average of the numbers as the appropriate single measure, how does this average increase in accuracy, if at all, as the number of observations is increased?

For example, suppose a certain length has been measured by four people who have found it to be 100 ft. 10 in, 100 ft., 99 ft. 7 in., and 100 ft. 3 in. The average is 100 ft. 2 in.

Suppose five more measurements are made giving 100 ft. 1 in., 99 ft. 9 in., 99 ft. 7 in., 100 ft. 5 in., 100 ft. 3 in. The average of the whole nine measurements is now 100 ft. 1 in. instead of 100 ft. 2 in. as with the first four measurements.

The question we ask is :

Is 100 ft. 1 in. a more accurate result than 100 ft. 2 in. ?

If so, how much more accurate can we expect it to be ?

In general we can see some justification for answering the first question in the affirmative. For, after all, if we think of all the measurements that might be taken, four of them might happen to be a very peculiar set, so that their average might be badly in error. On the other hand, while this might also be true of nine, it is less likely. One would expect a sample of nine to be nearer to the normal run of the numbers than a smaller sample of four readings. So what we are really asking is, How does the representative nature of the sample improve with the size of the sample ?

We shall try to answer this question in the following way. We shall suppose that we have a large collection of numbers, and that we draw a series of samples all of the same size. Each sample will give us an average. We shall then study these averages for all the samples of this size we can draw. These averages will therefore have a standard deviation which will show how the averages are scattered among themselves. What we want to know is how this standard deviation changes with the size of the sample. We have already seen in the examples of the last chapter that samples of two give a more packed distribution than individual samples. So already there is some evidence to show that as the size of the sample increases the standard deviation of the mean falls. We shall proceed to examine this question more generally.

Suppose there is a " population " of N numbers, viz. :

$$x_1, x_2, x_3, \ldots x_N$$

We take samples of n of these of the general type $x_i, x_j, x_k, \ldots x_n$. The mean of each such sample is

$$(x_i + x_j + x_k + \ldots + x_n)/n.$$

There will be as many such samples, and therefore as many such means, as there are ways of selecting n groups of the numbers out of the total N original numbers. Thus in all there will be $N!/n! (N-n)!$ samples and their means. What sort of population do these means give ?

(A) In the first place the mean of this derived population is the same as the mean of the original population.

Example : If the $N = 3$ the original population is x_1, x_2, x_3. The set of samples, say, two in number, is x_1, x_2 ; $x_2 x_3$; $x_1 x_3$. These give as means $(x_1 + x_2)/2$; $(x_2 + x_3)/2$; $(x_1 + x_3)/2$. The mean of these means is the sum of these divided by 3, that is $(x_1 + x_2 + x_3)/3$, or the mean of the original population.

We can see this quite generally in this way. Consider all the samples that contain x_1. We get these by taking x_1 away from the original N numbers and selecting $n - 1$ of the numbers out of the remaining $N - 1$.

Since there are $(N - 1)!/(n - 1)! \, (N - n)!$ ways of doing this, this will be the number of samples that contain x_1. Now we can write the mean of all the means of the samples in this way:

$$\left(\frac{x_1 + x_2 + \ldots + x_n}{n} + \frac{x_2 + x_3 + x_4 + \ldots}{n} + \ldots \right) \bigg/ \frac{N!}{n!(N - n)!}$$

since there are $N!/n!(N - n)!$ such samples.

In this the coefficient of x_1, since it occurs in $(N - 1)!/(n - 1)! \, (N - n)!$ terms, will be

$$\frac{(N-1)!}{(n-1)!(N-n)!} \cdot \frac{1}{n} \bigg/ \frac{N!}{n!(N-n)!} = \frac{(N-1)!}{(n-1)!(N-n)!} \cdot \frac{1}{n} \cdot \frac{n!(N-n)!}{N!}$$

$$= \frac{1}{N}$$

This must also be the coefficient of x_2, x_3, etc. Hence the mean of all the means is $(x_1 + x_2 + \ldots + x_N)/N =$ mean of original population.

(B) How are these means scattered about the mean of the whole population? What in fact is the standard deviation of these means, and how does it compare with the standard deviation of the original population? The reason we ask this question is this. Since the standard deviation measures the scatter about the mean, the standard deviation of the original population gives an overall measure of the extent to which an individual observation will differ from the mean. The standard deviation of the means of the samples will in the same sense give an overall measure of the extent to which a single mean will differ from the mean of the means, that is, from the mean of the original population. It will therefore indicate to us what we stand to gain in accuracy by taking a set of n observations and using *its* mean, instead of taking simply a single observation. We shall shortly illustrate this with a few examples.

We proceed, therefore, to calculate σ_n, the standard deviation of the system of means of all possible blocks of n of the observations.

For this purpose we shall calculate σ_n^2 by using a fictitious average of zero, and so using the formula

$$\sigma_n^2 = s_n^2 - M^2$$

where M is the mean of the original population, and s_n is the fictitious standard deviation of the means, estimated from the false average, viz. zero.

Thus $\qquad M = (x_1 + x_2 + \ldots + x_N)/N.$

s_n^2 is the sum of the squares of the means divided by the total number of samples, namely $N!/n! \, (N - n)!$

The sum of the squares of the means is

$$\left(\frac{x_1 + x_2 + \ldots}{n}\right)^2 + \left(\frac{x_1 + x_3 + \ldots}{n}\right)^2 + \left(\frac{x_2 + x_3 + \ldots}{n}\right)^2 + \ldots$$

where in each case there are n terms in each bracket. When this is expanded the terms will consist of an expression of the form

$$A(x_1^2 + x_2^2 + \ldots + x_N^2) + B(x_1 x_2 + x_1 x_3 + x_2 x_3 + \ldots)$$

where in the second expression all possible combinations of two items occur. The coefficients of the square terms are all the same since x_1 enters in exactly the same way as any other x. Let us find A, therefore, by discovering the coefficient of x_1^2, and B by obtaining the coefficient of $x_1 x_2$.

How many terms will contain x_1^2? As many times as x_1 occurs among the samples. As before, therefore, we set x_1 aside, and out of the remaining $N - 1$ members of the original population we select $n - 1$ members. This can be done in $(N - 1)!/(n - 1)!\,(N - n)!$ ways. Thus the coefficient of x_1^2 is

$$A = \frac{1}{n^2} \cdot \frac{(N - 1)!}{(n - 1)!(N - n)!} = \frac{1}{n} \cdot \frac{(N - 1)!}{n!\,(N - n)!}.$$

To find B we seek the coefficient of $x_1 x_2$. For this we have to inquire in how many samples both x_1 and x_2 occur, and for each of these we shall have $2x_1 x_2 / n^2$ arising when the squared brackets are multiplied out. The value of B is therefore $2/n^2$ times the number of occasions in which x_1 and x_2 occur together in a sample. To find this we set x_1 and x_2 aside out of the original population of N, leaving $N - 2$, and from these we select $n - 2$ other values of x. This can be done in $(N - 2)!/(n - 2)!\,(N - n)!$ ways. Hence the coefficient of $x_1 x_2$, viz. B, is

$$\frac{2}{n^2} \cdot \frac{(N - 2)!}{(n - 2)!(N - n)!} = \frac{2(n - 1)\,(N - 2)!}{n.n!\,(N - n)!}$$

The sum of the squares of the means is therefore

$$\frac{1}{n}\frac{(N - 1)!}{n!\,(N - n)!}(x_1^2 + x_2^2 + \ldots + x_N^2)$$

$$+ \frac{2(n - 1)\,(N - 2)!}{n.n!(N - n)!}\,(x_1 x_2 + x_2 x_3 + \ldots)$$

To obtain s_n^2 this has to be divided by the number of samples, viz. $N!/n!\,(N - n)!$

Thus

$$s_n^2 = \frac{1}{Nn}(x_1^2 + x_2^2 + \ldots + x_N^2) + \frac{2(n - 1)}{nN(N - 1)}\,(x_1 x_2 + x_2 x_3 + \ldots)$$

From this we have to subtract M^2, viz. :

$$(x_1 + x_2 + \ldots + x_N)^2/N^2$$

$$= (x_1^2 + x_1^2 + \ldots x_N^2)/N^2 + 2(x_1 x_2 + x_2 x_3 + \ldots)/N^2$$

Hence

$$\tau_n{}^2 = (x_1{}^2 + x_2{}^2 + \ldots + x_N{}^2)\left(\frac{1}{Nn} - \frac{1}{N^2}\right)$$
$$+ (x_1 x_2 + x_2 x_3 + \ldots)\left[\frac{2(n-1)}{nN(N-1)} - \frac{2}{N^2}\right]$$

$$= (x_1{}^2 + x_2{}^2 + \ldots + x_N{}^2)\,(N - n)/N^2 n$$
$$- 2(x_1 x_2 + x_2 x_3 + \ldots)\,(N - n)/N^2 n(N - 1).$$

How does this compare with the standard deviation of the original population ?

In this case, if S is the fictitious standard deviation corresponding to the fictitious average, viz. 0,

$$\sigma^2 = S^2 - M^2$$

$$= (x_1{}^2 + x_2{}^2 + \ldots + x_N{}^2)/N - (x_1 + x_2 + \ldots + x_N)^2/N^2$$

$$= \left(\frac{1}{N} - \frac{1}{N^2}\right)(x_1{}^2 + x_2{}^2 + \ldots) - \frac{2}{N^2}(x_1 x_2 + x_2 x_3 + \ldots)$$

$$= \frac{N-1}{N^2}(x_1{}^2 + x_2{}^2 + \ldots) - \frac{2}{N^2}(x_1 x_2 + x_2 x_3 + \ldots)$$

$$= \frac{n(N-1)}{(N-n)}\,\sigma_n{}^2.$$

It follows, therefore, that

$$\sigma_n{}^2 = \frac{N-n}{N-1} \cdot \frac{\sigma^2}{n}$$

The original population of size N is clearly in most cases very large. Indeed, if it consists of all the data that might be conceived as collected together, it is indefinitely large in general, compared with n, the size of the sample actually handled. In that case $(N - n)/(N - 1)$ is very nearly 1, and we may say that

$$\sigma_n^2 \text{ tends to } \sigma^2/n$$
or $\sigma_n = \sigma/\sqrt{n}$ when N is large.

What does this signify ?

We have to remember that σ is the standard deviation of the original population, and is therefore a constant number independent of n. Thus the result we have deduced shows that the standard deviation of the means of samples of size n diminishes as the square root of the size of the sample. Stated otherwise it would say that if we compare the accuracy of the average of two samples, one of which is, say, four times the size of the other, the average of the larger sample may be expected to be in error by half the amount by which the average of the smaller sample is in error.

Example : Let us verify the formula

$$\sigma_n^2 = \frac{N - n}{N - 1} \cdot \frac{\sigma^2}{n}$$

by means of the simple set 2, 4, 6. Here $N = 3$. The average is 4 and σ^2 is therefore

$$\sigma^2 = (4 + 4)/3 = 8/3$$

Now suppose $n = 2$. Hence all samples of two of these are 2, 4 ; 2, 6 ; 4, 6 giving as their averages 3, 4, 5. The average of these means is 4. Hence σ_n, the standard deviation of the averages, is given by

$$\sigma_n^2 = (1 + 1)/3 = 2/3$$

Also $$\frac{N - n}{N - 1} \cdot \frac{\sigma^2}{n} = \frac{3 - 2}{3 - 1} \cdot \frac{8}{3 \times 2} = \frac{2}{3}$$

which is the value of σ_n^2 as expected.

EXERCISES

1. Show that the mean value of 1, 2, 4, 8, 16, 32, 64, 128, 256, 512, 1024, 2048

  (i) is the same as the mean of the means of the first six and the last six ;

 (ii) is the same as the mean of the means of any three sets of 4 into which it can be sub-divided ;

(iii) is the same as the mean of the means of any four sets of 3 into which it can be subdivided ;

(iv) is the same as the mean of the means of any six sets of 2 into which it can be subdivided.

2. How many different samples of two numbers could be drawn from those given in Exercise 1 ?

3. How many different samples can be drawn of three of these numbers each containing 2048 ?

4. Verify the formula $\sigma_n{}^2 = (N - n)\sigma^2/(N - 1)n$ for the case of the sets

$$(i) \quad 2, 4, 8, 16$$
$$(ii) \quad 3, 9, 27$$

in each case taking samples of two.

5. Show that if N is large the error in writing $\sigma_n' = \sigma/\sqrt{n}$ is approximately $50(n - 1)/N$ per cent. of the value of σ_n .

6. According to the theory of the accuracy of the mean, $\sigma_n \sqrt{n}$ ought to remain approximately constant. From the following set of numbers choose six sets of pairs, six sets of three, six sets of four, six sets of five, and calculate $\sigma_n \sqrt{n}$ for the averages of each of the six sets :

19, 20, 21, 20, 22, 21, 20, 21, 21, 21, 20, 22, 22, 22, 21, 20, 22, 19, 23, 18, 19, 21, 21, 20, 21, 19, 20, 19, 20, 20, 20, 21.

(Note that in this $n = 2, 3, 4$, and 5 in succession.)

7. Show that if $n + 1$ readings are taken instead of n, the accuracy of the mean may be expected to increase by approximately $50/n$ per cent.

(397)

CHAPTER VII

RELATED MEASUREMENTS

In previous chapters we have been concerned with the various numbers that are found when successive attempts are made to measure the same thing. The " thing " was something which was regarded as having a unique value, or which was best described by means of a group of numbers. From these we settled a definite number to typify the group.

The next stage in our discussion brings us to the consideration of two numbers which are related to each other. As the one varies so does the other in some more or less definite way. The one is in fact a " function " of the other; the one depends on the other.

If we knew exactly how y depended on x, say, then of course every time we measure x we would know y. But usually the dependence is not known as accurately as that. We might know, for example, that y was proportional to x, but not know precisely by what x should be multiplied in order to find y. Thus we would say that $y = Ax$ where A is some unknown number. If we had a series of values of x obtained by measurement, and the values of y each corresponding to its value of x, we ought to be able to find A. If, of course, x and y were always exact we would require only one value of x and its corresponding value of y, for then we could find A from the fact that $A = y/x$. Unfortunately y and x are never perfect or unique, and so the series of measurements would give a whole series of different values of A corresponding to pairs of values of x and y. How are we to get the " best " value for A ?

Is it the average value of A, obtained by finding y/x for each pair of values x, y ? The answer would certainly be in the affirmative if A were directly measured, but this is not so. It is derived indirectly from two other numbers each directly measured.

A similar situation would arise if we knew that x and y are related by the formula

$$y = Ax + B$$

Here again if x and y were exact and unique, two pairs of values of x, y would suffice to find A and B, the unknown constants. But x and y are not unique, and so we are faced with the problem of finding the " best " values of A and B.

These are simple illustrations of a more general question, for clearly the functional relation between x and y might take a variety of forms other than those indicated above. For example, we might have

$$y = A + Bx + Cx^2$$

$$\text{or} \quad y = A + B/x$$

$$\text{or} \quad y = Ax^2 + B + C/x$$

and a large variety of other possibilities. These are not simply questions of mere mathematical interest, problems which the mathematician poses to himself. In every physical problem in which change is studied some general formula of this nature can be set out from theoretical analysis. It is the *exact* form that these experiments help us to obtain, for from them we derive the values of the constants such as A, B, and C.

For instance, if a gas be compressed in a cylinder at constant temperature, theory and experiment indicate that the relation between pressure and volume is very adequately expressed for a wide range of circumstances by the formula

$$\text{pressure} \times \text{volume} = \text{a constant}$$

or $x \times y = A$, where x is the pressure, say, in lb. per square inch, y is the volume in cubic inches, and A is some unknown constant. In the actual experiment a series of given pressures would be applied to the piston of the cylinder to compress the gas, and the compressed volume would be measured.   Thus

$$xy = A$$

$$\text{or} \quad y = A/x$$

would be the relation given by past theory and experiment, and from the various pairs of values of x and y obtained by the measurements of the compressed gas in the cylinder the " best " value of A would be found for this case.   General theory on the basis of past experience seeks to set up such formulæ in a wide variety of physical situations, and the constants in those formulæ have to be found from detailed experiments.   The determination of these constants is the problem of this chapter.   What we have done in earlier chapters is to treat the simplest possible case, where we seek the " best " value for a single constant which is directly measured.   The theoretical formula would be

$$x = A$$

and each experimental measurement of x determines a value of A.   The " best " value for A we found was the average of all the numbers so found.   Let us examine the method we have adopted in order to discover whether it can be extended to cover the more general type of formula to which we have just referred.

METHOD OF LEAST SQUARES

The formula we derived for the standard deviation σ in terms of a fictitious standard deviation s obtained by using a fictitious average A was

$$\sigma^2 = s^2 - (M - A)^2$$

where M was the true mean, or if we transpose

$$s^2 = \sigma^2 + (M - A)^2$$

On the right-hand side σ is a fixed number for a given set of measurements, for it is calculated from the actual average or mean M. The value of s therefore depends on A, the only number which might be changed on the right, where it enters in the term $(M - A)^2$. Thus s therefore reaches its smallest value when $(M - A)^2$ reaches its lowest value, but this smallest value is actually zero, and occurs when $M = A$. We conclude that the sum of the squares of the deviations of the readings from any chosen number is least when the number chosen is the average value.

It is worth summing up at this stage by stating two features that have shown themselves in our attempt to find typical numbers to represent a group of measurements :

(1) The first typical number (the mean) is that for which the sum of the deviations of the readings from it is zero.

(2) The mean is also the number from which the sum of the squares of the deviations from it reaches its lowest value. From this lowest value we have derived the number called the standard deviation.

If we look at (1) and (2) we can see that since the two typical numbers we have derived are the mean and the standard deviation, they are both really derivable from (2). We could have begun our discussion not by asking for which number the sum of the deviations is zero, as we did in (1), but for which number the sum of the squares of the deviations is least. This would lead us as an answer to the average or mean, which from the way in which it is found is such that the sum of its deviations is zero. From this principle, the standard deviation follows by definition. We conclude that essentially what we have done has been to seek a typical number M by applying the principle that the sum of the squares of the deviations from it shall be least. The next typical number σ is then found from this by direct definition. This principle is called the *Principle of Least Squares*. In later work we shall take this principle as our starting-off point, making it a fundamental assumption on which the whole theory will be based.

Application of Least Squares Method

Let us now turn to a problem to which we shall apply this principle.

A series of readings has been taken of two quantities which vary with each other. They may, for example, be the amount of stretch of a wire and the magnitude of the force stretching it. Let us call these x and y respectively. Therefore, we can plot the corresponding points in an ordinary x, y diagram. We shall assume that they are expected from the nature of the problem to lie on a straight line. For example, the stretch of the wire does increase proportionally to the force applied, provided we keep within certain narrow limits. From experimental data, however, we see that while the points lie very nearly on a straight line they do not do so exactly. Our problem is to determine the line that *best* fits these observations. We are not now seeking the " best " number to typify a set, but the " best " straight line to represent or typify a relation between two sets of numbers.

What do we mean by " best " ? In a general sense we can see that it implies finding the line that lies closest to the points as a group, but this in itself is too indefinite. We have to use some feature which is typical of the spread of the group of points about this line ; but this is precisely what the sum of the squares of the deviations offers as a measure. Accordingly, we will use as the test for the " best " straight line, that it is to be that one for which the sum of the squares of the deviations is least—the Principle of Least Squares.

For this purpose we shall define the deviation as the difference between the value of y at any position x, and the value it would have at that position if it fell exactly on the " best " line.

When the points lie fairly well about a line it is usually possible to draw the best line by eye, and in many cases this is the easiest and most convenient way to treat the question. Even a detailed calculation based on the method of least squares as developed below, in such cases does not make much difference to the line finally selected.

In the earlier case (Chapter III) where the values of y could be assumed to lie on a straight line parallel to the axis of x, that line passed through the average or mean value of these readings. Now we are to suppose that each y was an approximation not to $y =$ constant, but to $y = ax + b$. We will simplify our problem in the first place in the following way. Suppose that the measured values of x and of y have been tabulated, each x against each y, that the average x and average y have been found, and a new table drawn up which gives, in place of the original x and y, the difference between each of these and the average x and average y respectively. This is really equivalent to stating that a new pair of parallel axes, in place of the original x and y axes, will be taken through the centre of gravity or mean centre of the points. When the observations are now plotted on this diagram with these new x's and y's, they will lie roughly along a line $y = mx$. Let us suppose that this modified table of values is given as below :

x	x_1	x_2	x_3	. . .	x_n
y	y_1	y_2	y_3	. . .	y_n

We will assume, then, that the best line is given by $y = mx$ on this basis, and that it will be considered " best " when it lies at such an angle (determined by m) that the sum of the squares of the deviations of each plotted point $(x_1 y_1)$, $(x_2 y_2)$, . . . is least in the direction of y. This assumes, in fact, that each x measurement (*i.e.* deviation from the mean) involves no error in itself. This is equivalent to saying that we fix a value of x at which the y is to be measured. When x is x_1, the value of y is given by mx_1. The actual measured value is y_1. The difference is $mx_1 - y_1$. The sum of the squares of the deviations is therefore

$$(mx_1 - y_1)^2 + (mx_2 - y_2)^2 + \ldots + (mx_n - y_n)^2$$
$$= m^2(x_1{}^2 + x_2{}^2 + \ldots + x_n{}^2) - 2m(x_1 y_1 + x_2 y_2 + \ldots + x_n y_n)$$
$$+ (y_1{}^2 + y_2{}^2 + \ldots + y_n{}^2)$$

In this every symbol with the exception of m is known, and m determines the slope of the line. Our task is to find the value of m which makes this expression acquire its least value. To do this we will begin from the left by completing the square. For convenience, write :

$$X = x_1{}^2 + x_2{}^2 + \ldots + x_n{}^2$$
$$Y = y_1{}^2 + y_2{}^2 + \ldots + y_n{}^2$$
$$Z = x_1 y_1 + x_2 y_2 + \ldots + x_n y_n$$

The expression becomes

$$m^2 X - 2mZ + Y$$
$$= X\left(m^2 - 2m\frac{Z}{X}\right) + Y$$
$$= X\left(m^2 - 2m\frac{Z}{X} + \frac{Z^2}{X^2}\right) + Y - \frac{Z^2}{X}$$
$$= X\left(m - \frac{Z}{X}\right)^2 + \frac{XY - Z^2}{X}$$

Since the second term is fixed and the first term can never be negative but can be made to vary by changing the value of m, therefore the whole expression reaches its least value when $m = \dfrac{Z}{X}$, *i.e.* when

$$m = \frac{x_1 y_1 + x_2 y_2 + \ldots + x^n y^n}{x_1{}^2 + x_2{}^2 + \ldots + x_n{}^2}$$

This settles for us the slope of the " best " line passing through the point whose co-ordinates are the mean value of the x's and the mean value of the y's. The slope is itself expressed in this formula in terms of the squares and products of the deviations of the original readings from their respective means. The procedure to be followed in any particular case will be illustrated in the following example.

Example : An aeroplane starts from an aerodrome and climbs to 1,000 feet, when it proceeds to fly as nearly as possible in a straight line and with approximately constant speed over a distance of 50 miles. When 1,000 feet is reached over the base the petrol so far consumed is measured and a reading of the total petrol consumed is made at each 10 miles of the journey. Find in this case a suitable formula to represent the total quantity of petrol consumed at each stage of the journey. Here are the readings :

Miles from base at 1,000 ft. (D)	0	10	20	30	40	50
Petrol (P) consumed (gal.)	1·2	3·1	4·8	6·8	9·2	10·9

If these be represented on a diagram the following picture is obtained showing that the points lie approximately on a straight line.

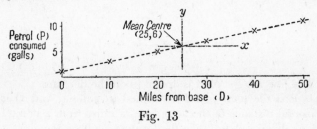

Fig. 13

The mean value of $D = \frac{1}{6}(0 + 10 + 20 + 30 + 40 + 50)$ = 25 miles. The mean value of P is $\frac{1}{6}(1·2 + 3·1 + 4·8 + 6·8 + 9·2 + 10·9) = \frac{1}{6} \times 36 = 6$ gallons.

We have now to draw up a table showing the deviations of these D's and P's from their respective means, viz. 25 and 6. Thus, in place of 0, 10, 20, 30, 40, 50, we now have $- 25$, $- 15$, $- 5, 5, 15, 25$, and for P, $- 4·8$, $- 2·9$, $- 1·2, 0·8, 3·2, 4·9$. These give our values of (x_1, y_1), (x_2, y_2) . . ., that is, $(- 25, - 4·8)$, $(- 15, - 2·9)$, $(- 5, - 1·2)$, $(5, 0·8)$, $(15, 3·2)$, $(25, 4·9)$.

Our formula for the slope m was

$$m = \frac{x_1 y_1 + x_2 y_2 + \ldots + x_n y}{x_1^2 + x_2^2 + \ldots + x_n}$$

Setting this out in tabular form, the calculation is as follows :

x	y	xy	x^2
-25	$-4 \cdot 8$	$120 \cdot 0$	625
-15	$-2 \cdot 9$	$43 \cdot 5$	225
-5	$-1 \cdot 2$	$6 \cdot 0$	25
5	$0 \cdot 8$	$4 \cdot 0$	25
15	$3 \cdot 2$	$48 \cdot 0$	225
25	$4 \cdot 9$	$122 \cdot 5$	625
Totals .		$344 \cdot 0$	1750

$$\text{Hence} \quad m = \frac{344}{1750} = 0 \cdot 1966$$

The line $y = 0 \cdot 1966 \, x$ is drawn in on the diagram.

If P is the total petrol consumed in gallons, and D is the horizontal distance of the aeroplane in miles from a point 1,000 feet up above its base, then the formula we have found is

$$P - 6 = 0 \cdot 1966(D - 25)$$

since x and y were measured from the mean value of P and D.

In this discussion we have assumed that the best line passes through the point whose co-ordinates are the mean of the x-readings and the mean of the y-readings. It is not difficult to prove that this must be so. Suppose the actual points specified by the pairs of readings are

$$(a_1, b_1), (a_2, b_2), (a_3, b_3) \ . \ . \ . \ (a_n, b_n)$$

so that the mean point is $(\bar{x}, \bar{y})$, where

$$n\bar{x} = a_1 + a_2 + \ . \ . \ . \ + a_n, \ n\bar{y} = b_1 + b_2 + \ . \ . \ . \ b_n.$$

Since in the earlier discussion $x_1, x_2, \ldots x_n, y_1, y_2 \ldots y_n$ were the measurements from the mean, it follows that

$$a_1 = \bar{x} + x_1, \quad a_2 = \bar{x} + x_2, \ldots a_n = \bar{x} + x_n$$
$$b_1 = \bar{y} + y_1, \quad b_2 = \bar{y} + y_2, \ldots b_n = \bar{y} + y_n$$

Let the best straight line be $y = mx + c$, then when the ordinate is b_1 at a_1, the line would have given $ma_1 + c$ as the best ordinate. The deviation is, therefore, $ma_1 + c - b_1$.

But
$$\begin{aligned} ma_1 + c - b_1 &= m(\bar{x} + x_1) + c - (\bar{y} + y_1) \\ &= m\bar{x} + c - \bar{y} + mx_1 - y_1 \end{aligned}$$

so that the sum of the squares of the deviations is

$$(m\bar{x} + c - \bar{y} + mx_1 - y_1)^2 + (m\bar{x} + c - \bar{y} + mx_2 - y_2)^2 + \ldots$$

We have to find that line which makes the sum of the squares of these deviations a minimum. The condition for this is that the differential coefficient of this series of squares has to be obtained with reference to c and m separately, and equated to zero. We will examine c only, for it suffices for our purpose.

Differentiating $(m\bar{x} + c - \bar{y} + mx_1 - y_1)^2$ with respect to c gives $2(m\bar{x} + c - \bar{y} + mx_1 - y_1)$. Thus the sum of the n differential coefficients gives

$$2n(m\bar{x}+c-\bar{y})+2m(x_1+x_2+ \ldots +x_n)-2(y_1+y_2+ \ldots +y_n)=0$$

But the sums of the deviations x_1, x_2, etc., and $y_1, y_2, \ldots$ are zero.

Thus $\quad m\bar{x} + c - \bar{y} = 0$

i.e. $\quad \bar{y} = m\bar{x} + c$

This shows that the point $(\bar{x}, \bar{y})$ lies on the line $y = mx + c$.

Hence the best line necessarily passes through the mean point.

Had we also differentiated the sum of the squares of the deviations with respect to m we could in that way have found an additional equation for m.

We can now write down the equation to the best line in general. Since it passes through $(\bar{x}, \bar{y})$ we can write it in the form

$$y - \bar{y} = m\,(x - \bar{x})$$

where m is the slope of the line already found to be

$$m = \frac{x_1 y_1 + x_2 y_2 + \ldots + x_n y_n}{x_1{}^2 + x_2{}^2 + \ldots + x_n{}^2}$$

In this $x_1, x_2, \ldots x_n, y_1, y_2, \ldots y_n$ are the deviations of the actual readings a and b from their respective means.

Standard Deviation about the Best Line

The sum of the squares of the deviations from the best straight line is

$$(m\bar{x} + c - \bar{y} + mx_1 - y_1)^2 + (m\bar{x} + c - \bar{y} + mx_2 - y_2)^2 + \ldots$$

We have just seen, however, that

$$m\bar{x} + c - \bar{y} = 0$$

Hence the sum of the squares is

$$(mx_1 - y_1)^2 + (mx_2 - y_2)^2 + \ldots + (mx_n - y_n)^2$$

$$= m^2(x_1{}^2 + x_2{}^2 + \ldots + x_n{}^2) - 2m(x_1 y_1 + x_2 y_2 + \ldots + x_n y_n)$$
$$+ (y_1{}^2 + y_2{}^2 + \ldots + y_n{}^2)$$

$$= m^2\,\mathrm{X} - 2m\,\mathrm{Z} + \mathrm{Y}$$

in our previous notation, where also we found that $m = \mathrm{Z}/\mathrm{X}$.

Thus, if σ is the standard deviation of these readings from the best line

$$n\sigma^2 = m^2\mathrm{X} - 2m\mathrm{Z} + \mathrm{Y}$$
$$= \mathrm{Z}^2/\mathrm{X} - 2\mathrm{Z}^2/\mathrm{X} + \mathrm{Y}$$
$$= \mathrm{Y} - \mathrm{Z}^2/\mathrm{X} = (\mathrm{XY} - \mathrm{Z}^2)/\mathrm{X}$$

If σ_x and σ_y are the standard deviations of the x and y co-ordinates respectively, and if we write

$$\sigma_{xy}{}^2 = \frac{1}{n}(x_1 y_1 + x_2 y_2 + \ldots + x_n y_n)$$

then $\qquad \sigma^2 = (\sigma_x{}^2 \sigma_y{}^2 - \sigma_{xy}{}^4)/\sigma_x{}^2$

Non-Linear Relations

The method of least squares can now be extended to the case where the experimental points do not lie along a straight line but follow some other law. We write down the equation to the curve in its general form, set out the deviations of the y-ordinates from those that would have been obtained if the readings had fallen exactly on the ideal curve, square these deviations, and find the values of the constants in the general equation that make the sum of the squares of the deviations a minimum. In general this is best done by means of the differential calculus.

Example 1 : We illustrate with a simple case. Suppose the following readings have been obtained in a case where it is known that the general law is of the form, $y = A + Bx^2$,

x	0	1	2	3
y	1	6	20	48

We assume that the values of x are correct but those of y are subject to error. Thus the correct values of y at $x = 0, 1, 2, 3$, are respectively

$$A, \quad A + B, \quad A + 4B, \quad A + 9B$$

as derived from the equation $y = A + Bx^2$.

Hence the deviations are respectively

$$A - 1, \quad A + B - 6, \quad A + 4B - 20, \quad A + 9B - 48$$

Accordingly, to find A and B we have to make the sum of the squares of these deviations a minimum. Thus the expression

$$(A-1)^2+(A+B-6)^2+(A+4B-20)^2+(A+9B-48)^2$$

is to be a minimum. This demands that since it must be a minimum for variations both in A and in B separately, that the differential coefficient of this with respect to A and also with respect to B must be zero. This provides us with the following two relations :

$$2(A-1) + 2(A+B-6) + 2(A+4B-20) + 2(A+9B-48) = 0$$
$$2(A+B-6) + 8(A+4B-20) + 18(A+9B-48) = 0$$

These reduce at once to the two equations for A and B, viz.

$$4A + 14B = 75$$
$$A + 7B = 37,$$

giving $\qquad A = 0\cdot5 \qquad B = 5\cdot21$

Thus the " best " equation of the type $y = A + Bx^2$ for these observations would be

$$y = 0\cdot5 + 5\cdot21x^2$$

At	$x =$	0	1	2	3
this gives	$y =$	$0\cdot5$	$5\cdot71$	$21\cdot34$	$47\cdot39$
in place of	$y =$	1	6	20	48

Example 2 : Suppose the idealized law is given by $pv = A$ where p is the pressure of a gas, when its volume is v, and A is some constant.

Our problem is to determine the " best " value for the constant A when a series of corresponding values of p and v have been derived experimentally. In illustration let us suppose the following pairs of values have been found :

$$(p_1, v_1), (p_2, v_2), (p_3, v_3).$$

When the volume is v_1, the " true " value of p from the formula would be A/v_1. Its actual value is p_1. Hence the deviation is $A/v_1 - p_1$. Applying this in each case we find for the sum of the squares of the deviations

$$(A/v_1 - p_1)^2 + (A/v_2 - p_2)^2 + (A/v_3 - p_3)^2$$

and A has so to be chosen as to reduce this to a minimum. Differentiating, therefore, with respect to A, we find

$$(A/v_1 - p_1)/v_1 + (A/v_2 - p_2)/v_2 + (A/v_3 - p_3)/v_3 = 0$$

$$i.e. \quad A = (p_1/v_1 + p_2/v_2 + p_3/v_3)/(1/v_1{}^2 + 1/v_2{}^2 + 1/v_3{}^2)$$

This determines the " best " value for the constant A on the assumption that the readings are regarded as derived from the equation $pv = A$, but that p only is subject to error.

EXERCISES

1. A wire was stretched by the application of 1 lb. weights on a series of occasions, and the extension noted. The following readings were obtained :

Load (lb.)	1	2	3	4	5	6	7	8
Extension (cm.)	0·07	0·13	0·19	0·24	0·31	0·37	0·43	0·50

Find the equation to the best straight line fitting these observations, and find what the extension would be if a load of 10 lb. were suspended by the wire. Draw a graph showing the points and the line.

2. In an experiment the following results were obtained :

P (lb.)	11	13	15	17	19	21
F (lb.)	2·5	2·8	3·0	3·5	3·9	4·3

Assuming that P is devoid of error, fit a straight line by the method of least squares, and tabulate the corrected values of F.

3. The following are the values found for the respective pressures and volumes of a gas at constant temperature :

p (in lb. per sq. ft.)	15	20	25	30	35
v (cub. ft.)	0·31	0·23	0·19	0·16	0·14

Assuming that errors occur only in v, and that a theoretical law in this case is $p=A/v$, plot p against $1/v$, and find the best straight line that lies among the points.
Hence find the best form for the law.

4. By the method of least squares fit a parabola $y = Ax^2 + B$ to the points

x	0·5	1·0	1·5	2·0	2·5
y	0·48	3·61	8·51	15·75	24·28

5. Use the method of least squares to find the most suitable values for a and b in order that $y = ax^2 + b/x$ may approximately assume the values given below :

x	1	2	3	4
y	−1·51	0·99	3·88	7·66

6. By the method of least squares, find a formula of the type $y = a + bx^2$ to represent approximately the following values of y :

x	0	1	2	3	4	5
y	− 1·01	0·02	2·98	8·01	14·89	24·11

7. Use the method of least squares to determine A and B in the formula $y = Ax + Bx^2$ for the following observations :

x	1	2	3	4	5
y	1·8	5·1	8·9	14·1	19·8

From the formula obtained, calculate the values of y when $x = 1, 2, 3, 4, 5$.

8. If $y_1, y_2, \ldots y_n$ be n experimentally determined values of y at the exact times $t_1, t_2, \ldots t_n$, show how to use the method to determine A and B when the relation

$$y = At^2 + B/t^2$$

is believed to hold between y and t.

9. Use the method of least squares to determine the constants A and B in the formula

$$y = A + Bx^2$$

representing the data

x	0·5	1·1	1·4	4·3	5·0
y	2·75	1·9	1·1	− 15·5	− 22·0

in which y only is subject to accidental error.

CHAPTER VIII

CORRELATION: THE MEASURE OF TRENDS

WE began this book by drawing a distinction between two types of measurement. One type, always regarded as in error, sought to express something which possessed a unique value; the other, always regarded as true, provided information about something that was necessarily represented by a set of statistics, or by a group of measurements. The approach to both tended to converge in the sense that for the second type we chose the mean or average as the typical value for the set, and so for some purposes at any rate we could use a unique value to represent that set. Closer study, of course, demanded an investigation of the spread about this mean value, and this we did by means of frequency curves and standard deviations. In the foregoing chapter we passed on to an examination of a rather similar problem. There we were concerned with the relation between two sets of numbers which varied one with the other. Again there was implied in what we were doing that there existed a unique relation between them. For example, we have sought for the precise relation between the distance flown by an aeroplane and the amount of petrol consumed. In applying the method of least squares to this problem we have made the assumption that although every measurement involved might be in error, an idealized law relating the two quantities, and these two quantities only, did exist. In the corresponding case of a number of measurements of a unique quantity we used the same method, and that led us to the average or mean as the " best " value. In the last chapter we were led to the " best " straight line relation, or to the best one of a series of possible theoretical relations. We can now therefore turn to the problem where it is not possible to say that a unique relation exists between the two varying quantities. If x and y are the two numbers, every pair of values of x and y taken together provides us with definite, and in its own way accurate, information of the relation, whatever it is, that exists between them, but that relation is not unique. Each value of x is simply one of a set that might have occurred about some central value of x, and each value of y associated with each value of x is also one of a set that might have occurred about some central value of y. And this would be true over the whole range of x, and over the whole range of y. Thus, if we were to plot the many points (x, y) on an ordinary diagram, the corresponding points would be scattered over a fairly wide region. The extent of this scattering shows, in the first place, that we are not dealing with the type of case already discussed, where we could assume a unique relation as existing between x and y over the whole range. For example, we might inquire whether there existed any relation between the heights and weights of a group of people. We could then collect together the data arranged in two columns, the first column showing *heights*, and opposite each height in the second column we would write down the *weight* of the person of that height. Points plotted on a diagram, with heights horizontally set out and weights vertically set out, would show a distribution of points that lie over a fairly wide area. It would not be easy to say that there existed a unique relation between the two, but that some sort of relation did exist is also fairly evident.

How is this relation to be expressed ?

Now in this illustration we might quite well have two people with different heights but the same weights, or two people with the same heights but different weights. Neither weights nor heights, as it were, correspond to unique measurements. Between the two extreme cases we have mentioned, however, there stands an intermediate one. We might have unique values horizontally and a series of statistical values vertically. For example, if we were recording the volume of water that flows over a certain dam every twenty-four hours, we could make little mistake in the measurement of the twenty-four hours interval, but the actual volume of water that flowed might vary considerably, dependent as it would be on the rainfall and other factors over which we have no control. Over a certain period of the year this might increase regularly, but the regularity would be irregular for the reason we have stated. In such a case we might expect some relation to show itself between the volume of water and the time of flow, but it would still not be a simple unique relation, although we might expect it to be a great deal more precise than would be the case when both the horizontal and vertical measurements in the corresponding diagram are liable to statistical fluctuations.

We begin, therefore, with a study of this type of case.

A member of the Home Guard tests his accuracy at musketry by firing at a target after running at the double, and notes the number of shots that fall *outside* a small circle surrounding the bull's eye. Here are the results he obtained taking in each case ten shots :

No. of wide shots out of 10	No. of minutes at the double
0	0
2	1
5	2
4	3
6	4
8	5
7	6

Is there any relation indicated between the number of shots that fall wide and the number of minutes previously run at the double ? If he were to run for eight minutes, what is likely to be the number of wide shots, estimated on the basis of his performance ? It is clear that in a broad general way the number of wide shots increases with the time run, but at what rate does it increase? The first step is clearly to plot on a diagram the number of wide shots against the minutes run at the double. We obtain the following diagram :

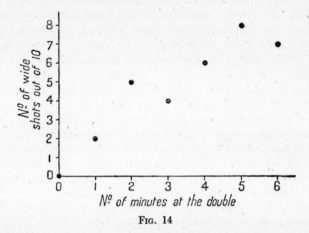

Fɪɢ. 14

It can hardly be said that these lie closely along a straight line, but nevertheless the general trend is obvious. We could say that there is a *correlation* between the two features.

If we attempt to draw a straight line that lies evenly among the points, a variety of positions for these lines can be found. It would be very difficult to say that one more closely represented the results than the other. We could think of the two extreme views. A man might run at the double on various occasions, say for three minutes, and on each occasion try his shots at the target. While there would be no mistake or variation in the number of minutes run, there would certainly be a variation from one time to the next of the number of wide shots, although this might not be very large. In this case we could say that while the number of minutes run was accurate, the " error " or variation in the results showed itself in the number of wide shots. We could take the other extreme view and ask, for example,

how many minutes a man has to run in order that only five of
his shots should be wide ? On one occasion it might turn out
to be two minutes, and on another perhaps three or more minutes.
Here there is no variation in the number of shots wide ; the
" error," as it were, occurs in the number of minutes run. It
is clear that in any actual case both these " errors " may
enter together, but the two points of view we have suggested
indicate a method of disentangling the features of this *scatter
diagram.*

Let us apply these principles in order to find two lines that
correspond to these extreme viewpoints. In one case we shall
regard the numbers that appear on the horizontal line as being
precise measurements, while those that appear vertically are
subject to error, and in the other case we shall regard the numbers
that appear on the vertical line as accurate, while those on the
horizontal line are subject to " errors." To find these lines in
each case we shall use the method of least squares.

We begin by assuming that the characteristic plotted along
the x-direction is accurately specified, and that the variations
occur in the y direction only. If we measure everything from
the mean value of the x and the mean value of the y readings,
then by the method of least squares we can find the best line
that passes through this mean point, and fits the observations
most closely. If x and y are the deviations from the mean readings
in these two directions, then, as we have seen in the last chapter,
the best line is given by

$$y = \frac{x_1 y_1 + x_2 y_2 + \ldots + x_n y_n}{x_1^2 + x_2^2 + x_3^2 \ldots + x_n^2} \, x$$

In this equation (x_1, y_1), (x_2, y_2) . . . are all measured from
the mean x and mean y.

$$i.e. \quad y = \frac{\sum\limits_{r=1}^{n} x_r y_r}{\sum\limits_{r=1}^{n} x_r^2} \, x$$

Now the standard deviation of x_1, x_2, . . . x_n which we may write σ_x, is given by $\sigma_x^2 = \dfrac{\Sigma x_1^2}{n}$ and the standard deviation of y_1, y_2, . . . y_n is given by $\sigma_y^2 = \dfrac{\Sigma y_1^2}{n}$. On this basis we can write the equation to the best line obtained by the method of least squares in the form

$$\frac{y}{\sigma_y} = \frac{\Sigma xy}{\sqrt{(\Sigma x^2 \Sigma y^2)}} \cdot \frac{x}{\sigma_x}$$
$$= r \cdot \frac{x}{\sigma_x}$$

where r is the coefficient of $\dfrac{x}{\sigma_x}$.

This tells us that if we take a deviation of x from the mean so that $\dfrac{x}{\sigma_x} = 1$, the deviation of y from the mean is r times its standard deviation, for in this equation x and y are associated with their own special standard deviations σ_x and σ_y. Therefore r is a number which measures the extent of the change occurring in y (expressed as a proportion of its standard deviation) for a corresponding change in x (measured in terms of its standard deviation), where r is written for convenience in place of $\dfrac{\Sigma xy}{\sqrt{(\Sigma x^2 \Sigma y^2)}}$. This is a number, for if x and y were lengths, Σxy would be the sum of a series of areas, Σx^2 would be an area, and the square root of Σx^2 would therefore be a length, as would also be the square root of Σy^2. The square root of $\Sigma x^2 \Sigma y^2$ would therefore also be an area ; r therefore tells us *how many times* the area in the numerator is greater than the area in the denominator. It is therefore simply a number, and its value will be quite independent of the terms in which x and y are measured. This would be equally true whatever x and y represented. The equation $\dfrac{y}{\sigma_y} = r \cdot \dfrac{x}{\sigma_x}$ suggests by its form that instead of plotting

y against x it would have been better first to calculate σ_x and σ_y, and then plot $\dfrac{y}{\sigma_y}$ (say Y) against $\dfrac{x}{\sigma_x}$ (say X). Thus we would have the simple relation

$$Y = rX$$

This tells us that if we take a deviation from the mean corresponding to a value X of, say, unit amount, the deviation of Y is r. r is therefore a number which measures the extent of the change occurring in y (expressed as a proportion of its standard deviation) for a corresponding change in x (measured in terms of its standard deviation).

Now suppose we invert the picture and we regard the y's as accurately specified and the x's as subject to variation. We could then take the same points in the diagram and attempt to find the best straight line $x = My$ which fitted the points most closely. In general this will be a different straight line from the previous one, but it will pass through the same mean point. We can write down the equation to this straight line at once if we notice that in its final form (expressed in terms of standard deviations) it was symmetrical about x and y. The equation in fact becomes

$$\frac{x}{\sigma_x} = r \cdot \frac{y}{\sigma_y} \quad \text{or} \quad X = rY$$

and now r is a measure of the change produced in y (expressed in terms of the standard deviation) for a unit change in x (expressed in terms of the standard deviation). Thus in both equations r measures the extent of the change in the one due to a change in the other. In the first case it is the slope of the line with respect to the horizontal X axis and in the case of the second line it represents *its* slope with respect to the Y axis. The two lines, therefore, are equally inclined to the axis which in each case was regarded as representing quantities devoid of error.

When the two lines fall together they are each naturally inclined at an angle of 45° to their X or Y axis. Their slope is then 1 and $r = 1$. Notice, therefore, that $r = 1$ corresponds to the case where there is perfect correlation between the two variables X and Y, and therefore between x and y; r itself is called the *coefficient of correlation*. It is clear from the foregoing that r is in general a number less than 1, and is taken to provide a measure of the degree of relation between x and y.

When a change in X corresponds to no significant change in Y, r is zero, and this would also correspond to a case, therefore, where a change in Y corresponds to no significant change in X. Thus $r = 0$ corresponds to the case where there is no relation whatever between X and Y, that is, between x and y. The two are quite independent. Summing up, therefore, we can say that r measures the amount of dependence of y on x, and x on y. When $r = 1$ they are completely bound together, or appear to be completely dependent one on the other, and when $r = 0$ they are completely independent. The case $r = 0$ will clearly correspond in the X, Y diagram to the two lines at right angles.

It should be noticed that r is not necessarily a positive number. A positive change in X might correspond to a negative change in Y, in which case r is negative, and we say that there is a *negative correlation* between x and y of the amount r. The line which passes through the mean point and corresponds to the extreme case where x is assumed to be accurate, is referred to as the *line of regression of y on x*. On the other hand, when y is assumed to be accurate, the other extreme line is called the *line of regression of x on y*.

Example : We will now work out in detail the example given at the beginning of this chapter. We require, first of all, the average number of wide shots and the average number of minutes run at the double. The average number of minutes run at the double is $(0 + 1 + 2 + 3 + 4 + 5 + 6)$ divided by 7, because there are seven pairs of observations. This equals $21/7 = 3$. Similarly the average number of wide shots is $(0 + 2 + 5 + 4 + 6 + 8 + 7)/7 = 32/7 = 4\cdot57$. Using the notation we have adopted in the theory, x and y will represent the deviation of the number of minutes run and the number of wide shots from their respective averages, so that we have :

x	y	xy	x^2	y^2
− 3	− 4·57	+ 13·71	9	20·885
− 2	− 2·57	+ 5·14	4	6·605
− 1	+ 0·43	− 0·43	1	0·185
0	− 0·57	0	0	0·325
+ 1	+ 1·43	+ 1·43	1	2·045
+ 2	+ 3·43	+ 6·86	4	11·765
+ 3	+ 2·43	+ 7·29	9	5·905
		+ 34·43	28	47·715
		− 0·43		
		+ 34		

Thus we have the following results : $\Sigma xy = 34$, $\Sigma x^2 = 28$, and $\Sigma \bar{y}^2 = 47\cdot715$. Hence, to find the coefficient of correlation (r) we calculate

$$r = \frac{\Sigma xy}{\sqrt{(\Sigma x^2 \cdot \Sigma y^2)}}$$
$$= \frac{34}{\sqrt{(28)(47\cdot715)}}$$
$$= 0\cdot93$$

so that the correlation is very high.

In addition we calculate the standard deviation of the x's (σ_x) and of the y's (σ_y)

$$\sigma_x{}^2 = (\Sigma x^2)/n = 28/7 = 4$$

so that $\sigma_x = 2$ (in the units in which x is expressed, *i.e.* minutes). Similarly $\sigma_y{}^2 = (\Sigma y^2)/n = 47\cdot715/7 = 6\cdot816$, so that $\sigma_y = 2\cdot611$ shots.

In order to draw the regression lines we need to draw up a new table, plotting $X\left(=\dfrac{x}{\sigma_x}\right)$ and $Y\left(=\dfrac{y}{\sigma_y}\right)$. We have the following table :

X	Y
— 1·5	— 1·75
— 1·0	— 0·99
— 0·5	+ 0·16
0	— 0·22
+ 0·5	+ 0·55
+ 1·0	+ 1·31
+ 1·5	+ 0·93

The line of regression of y on x is therefore given by

$$Y = rX$$

in this case $Y = 0.93X$, and the line of regression of x on y is $X = 0.93Y$.

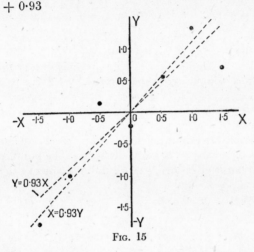

Fig. 15

It should be noted that in this example the coefficient of correlation is very nearly 1 (indicating apparently close connection between the two variables), and hence the two regression lines lie close together, both being inclined at very nearly 45° to either axis.

USE OF THE COEFFICIENT OF CORRELATION

The calculation of r has suggested for us that a linear relation approximately exists between the time of running and the number of wide shots. The relation, it will be remembered, was of the form

$$Y = rX$$

We ask, suppose the time of running be increased by one minute, how may we expect the number of wide shots to increase?

Now it is clear that any increase in X corresponds to an increase of r times this amount in Y. If x be increased by one minute, by how much does X increase? Now $X = \dfrac{x}{\sigma_x}$ and $\sigma_x = 2$, therefore the increase in X is $\frac{1}{2}$. Hence the increase in Y is $\frac{1}{2}(r) = \frac{1}{2}(0 \cdot 93) = 0 \cdot 465$, but $Y = \dfrac{y}{\sigma_y}$ so that $y = Y\sigma_y$, and $\sigma_y = 2 \cdot 611$.

Hence the increase in y is $0 \cdot 465 \, \sigma_y$,
i.e. $(0 \cdot 465) \, . \, (2 \cdot 611) = 1 \cdot 214$. Thus we may expect the number of wide shots to increase on the average by $1 \cdot 214$.

Example 1 : Is there any correlation between height and visual power?

Ten people of various heights as under were requested to read the letters on a card at 25 yards distance. The number of letters correctly read is given below, with the subsequent calculation :

Height	No. of letters	x (in.)	y (No. of letters)	$x \times y$	x^2	y^2
5′ 1″	11	− 7	− 3	+ 21	49	9
5′ 3″	17	− 5	+ 4	− 20	25	16
5′ 6″	19	− 2	+ 5	− 10	4	25
5′ 7″	14	− 1	0	0	1	0
5′ 8″	8	0	− 6	0	0	36
5′ 9″	15	+ 1	+ 1	+ 1	1	1
5′ 10″	20	+ 2	+ 6	+ 12	4	36
5′ 11″	6	+ 3	− 8	− 24	9	64
6′ 0″	18	+ 4	+ 4	+ 16	16	16
6′ 1″	12	+ 5	− 2	− 10	25	4
Aver. = 5′ 8″	Aver. 14	0	0	$\Sigma xy = 14$	$\Sigma x^2 = 134$	$\Sigma y^2 = 207$

$$r = \frac{\Sigma xy}{\sqrt{(\Sigma x^2 \cdot \Sigma y^2)}} = \frac{-14}{\sqrt{134 \times 207}}$$
$$= -0 \cdot 084$$

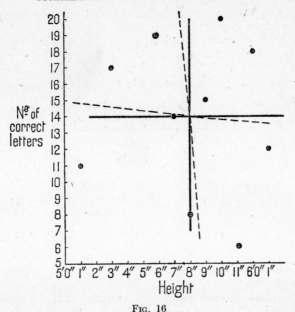

Fɪɢ. 16

There is therefore no perceptible correlation. In Chapter **X.** we shall discuss the significance of such correlations.

A rapid estimate of the correlation coefficient can be made in the following way. Find the average values of the x's and of the y's, viz. $\bar{x}$ and $\bar{y}$. Plot the point $(\bar{x}, \bar{y})$ on a diagram. Plot the points (x, y) on the same diagram ignoring those that lie in the neighbourhood of $(\bar{x}, \bar{y})$. Take the two points farthest removed from $(\bar{x}, \bar{y})$, which when joined to the latter give a *rough* measure of the angular spread of the points. The cosine of this angle is approximately the correlation coefficient.

Example 2 :	x'	5	7	3	2	1	0
	y'	7	5	4	1	1	0

Here x', y' are the original readings.　We now find the means :

$$\bar{x} = (5 + 7 + 3 + 2 + 1 + 0)/6 = 3$$
$$\bar{y} = (7 + 5 + 4 + 1 + 1 + 0)/6 = 3$$

Writing the deviations of x' and y' from the average as x and y we get

x	2, 4, 0, -1, -2, -3
y	4, 2, 1, -2, -2, -3

Thus
$$\Sigma x^2 = 4 + 16 + 0 + 1 + 4 + 9 = 34$$
$$\Sigma y^2 = 16 + 4 + 1 + 4 + 4 + 9 = 38$$
$$\Sigma xy, = 8 + 8 + 0 + 2 + 4 + 9 = 31$$

$$r = \frac{31}{\sqrt{34 \times 38}} = 0 \cdot 87$$

This, then, is the actual correlation coefficient, calculated in the usual way.

To obtain a quick but rough estimate of this we plot the mean point $(3, 3)$ on a diagram.　The two points farthest removed from $(3, 3)$ are $(5, 7)$ and $(7, 5)$.　When these are joined to $(3, 3)$ two lines are obtained which approximately give the angular spread of the points.　If this angle be measured with a protractor, and its cosine found in a book of tables, it will be seen to be $0 \cdot 8$ instead of the accurate value $0 \cdot 87$.

It is not difficult to see why this is so.　If $x_1 x_2 \ldots x_n$ and $y_1 y_2 \ldots y_n$ are the deviations from the averages of the x's and the y's, then

$$r = \frac{\Sigma xy}{\sqrt{(\Sigma x^2 \Sigma y^2)}}$$

Suppose x_1 and x_2 are the two largest values of the x's, and y_1 and y_2 are the two largest values of the y's, and suppose $x_1 y_1$ and $x_2 y_2$ are either both positive or both negative, then the numerator of the expression for r is approximately $x_1 y_1 + x_2 y_2$, while the denominator is approximately $\sqrt{(x_1{}^2 + x_2{}^2)(y_1{}^2 + y_2{}^2)}$. This means that the angle of spread must lie entirely either in the first and third quadrant, or in the second and fourth quadrant, otherwise $x_1 y_1$ and $x_2 y_2$ will not have the same sign. Now suppose also that the two lines enclosing the angle of spread are equally inclined to the x and y axes respectively, that is to say, the two lines lie evenly on each side of the line $y = x$ or $y = -x$. If this is so we may take $x_2 = y_1$, and $y_2 = x_1$, so that the denominator becomes $\sqrt{(x_1{}^2 + y_1{}^2)(x_2{}^2 + y_2{}^2)}$. Thus approximately

$$r = \frac{x_1}{\sqrt{(x_1{}^2 + y_1{}^2)}} \cdot \frac{x_2}{\sqrt{(x_2{}^2 + y_2{}^2)}} + \frac{y_1}{\sqrt{(x_1{}^2 + y_1{}^2)}} \cdot \frac{y_2}{\sqrt{(x_2{}^2 + y_2{}^2)}}$$

$$= \cos A \cdot \cos B + \sin A \cdot \sin B$$

where A and B are the angles made by the lines with the axis of x.

Thus $\qquad r = \cos (A - B) = \cos \theta$

where θ is the angle between the two lines.

SHORT METHOD OF CALCULATING THE CORRELATION COEFFICIENT

With the notation we adopted earlier in this chapter, the coefficient of correlation (r) was given by

$$r = \frac{\Sigma xy}{\sqrt{(\Sigma x^2 \Sigma y^2)}}$$

where Σxy, or to be more precise $\sum\limits_{r=1}^{n} x_r y_r$, represented the sum of the products of each x-deviation from its mean and each y-deviation from its mean. It is often laborious to work out each deviation from its mean, and a short method may be adopted analagous to the short method of finding the mean and the standard deviation, whereby time may be saved.

Suppose the original values of the two correlated variables are $X_1, X_2, \ldots X_N$ and $Y_1, Y_2, \ldots Y_N$ with means $\bar{X}$ and $\bar{Y}$ and standard deviations σ_X and σ_Y respectively. Then

$$\bar{X} = \frac{\Sigma X_r}{N}, \ \bar{Y} = \frac{\Sigma Y_r}{N}, \sigma_X{}^2 = \frac{\Sigma(X_r - \bar{X})^2}{N} \text{ and } \sigma_Y{}^2 = \frac{\Sigma(Y_r - \bar{Y})^2}{N}$$

Then, since $x_1 = X_1 - \bar{X}, y_1 = Y_1 - \bar{Y}$, etc., the correlation coefficient becomes

$$r = \frac{\Sigma(X_r - \bar{X})(Y_r - \bar{Y})}{\sqrt{\{\Sigma(X_r - \bar{X})^2 \cdot \Sigma(Y_r - \bar{Y})^2\}}}$$

$$= \frac{\Sigma(X_r Y_r - \bar{X} Y_r - \bar{Y} X_r + \bar{X}\bar{Y})}{\sqrt{(N\sigma_X{}^2 \cdot N\sigma_Y{}^2)}}$$

$$= \frac{\Sigma X_r Y_r - \bar{X}\Sigma Y_r - \bar{Y}\Sigma X_r + N\bar{X}\bar{Y}}{N\sigma_X\sigma_Y}$$

But $\Sigma Y_r = N\bar{Y}$ and $\Sigma X_r = N\bar{X}$

$$\therefore \ r = \frac{\Sigma X_r Y_x - N\bar{X}\bar{Y} - N\bar{X}\bar{Y} + N\bar{X}\bar{Y}}{N\sigma_X\sigma_Y}$$

$$= \frac{\Sigma X_r Y_r - N\bar{X}\bar{Y}}{N\sigma_X\sigma_Y}$$

It is sometimes very much quicker to calculate $\Sigma X_r Y_r$, the sum of the products of corresponding X and Y observations, *as they stand* than to calculate Σxy, the sum of the products of corresponding deviations from their respective means.

EXERCISE A

1. The figures give the ages of 10 boys when they left off studying and the salary per annum each was earning when he reached the age of 30 :

Age (years)	15	15	16	17	17	18	19	20	21	22
Salary (£)	210	190	270	200	310	300	340	320	400	360

Draw the scatter diagram, find the coefficient of correlation, and state your deductions.

2. Ten students of different ages were given a test on which they received a percentage mark. The figures giving their marks and ages are

Age (years and months)	17 10	18 0	18 10	19 1	19 5	20 4	20 8	21 6	21 10	22 6
Marks %	86	82	64	74	67	77	94	79	62	85

Work out the coefficient of correlation, and state your deductions.

3. The monthly profits of a small business for two years are as follows :

	Jan.	Feb.	Mar.	Apl.	May	June	July	Aug.	Sep.	Oct.	Nov.	Dec.
1936 (£)	18	3	7	10	16	29	30	24	12	12	12	19
1937 (£)	15	2	3	10	21	32	38	27	10	13	18	15

Draw a graph from these data ; find the coefficient of correlation.

4. Index numbers of Retail Prices of Food for Great Britain and for the United States of America are given for seven years. Find the arithmetic mean index number, and standard deviation for each of the two countries, and hence the coefficient of correlation.

	1920	1922	1924	1926	1928	1930	1932
Gt. Britain	256	176	170	164	157	145	126
U.S.A.	196	170	174	178	173	164	134

5. From the following table compute the coefficient of correlation between savings-bank deposits and strikes and lock-outs in the United States over the period 1916 to 1922 inclusive :

Date	Savings-bank deposits in in billions of dollars	Strikes and lock-outs in thousands
1916	5·1	3·8
1917	5·4	4·4
1918	5·5	3·3
1919	5·9	3·6
1920	6·5	3·3
1921	6·0	2·3
1922	7·2	1·0

6. The following figures give the number of suicides among men and women for the years 1922–32. Determine the correlation coefficient between them :

Year	1922	1923	1924	1925	1926	1927	1928	1929	1930	1931	1932
Men	2817	2887	2635	2852	3099	3458	3409	3480	3527	3624	4050
Women	1059	1062	1085	1232	1350	1449	1473	1504	1524	1533	1689

7. Examine the following data for a possible correlation between x and y ; and determine the correlation coefficient.

x	124	109	125	78	123	127	170	97	140
y	13·3	14·9	14·6	7·1	13·6	16·2	36·6	6·3	29

ARRANGEMENT IN RANKS

The results of many examinations or tests of a competitive nature are finally set out, not in the actual marks obtained but in an *order of merit*, viz. 1st, 2nd, 3rd, 4th, 5th, etc., on the list. When this is done the candidates are said to have been arranged in *ranks*. Thus, here are the actual marks of ten candidates with their ranks written below the marks :

A	B	C	D	E	F	G	H	I	J	
70	64	82	30	45	45	77	58	40	60	Marks
3	4	1	10	$7\frac{1}{2}$	$7\frac{1}{2}$	2	6	9	5	Rank

Notice that instead of bracketing E and F as 7th equal, or 7th and 8th together, we rank them each $7\frac{1}{2}$, which seems reasonable since they both occupy the 7th and 8th places.

It is clear that those interested in training and education are likely to be concerned with correlations between the rank obtained by a candidate in one examination with that obtained by him in another. For example, we might ask whether a student who ranks high at theory ranks as high at practice—on the average. Are students good at mathematics also good at physics, or at chemistry, or at languages ?

Correlation by Ranks

When the correlation is required between two series of numbers, a very rapid approximation to r is found by ranking each set in order of magnitude and noticing the difference in rank of each item. The sum of the squares of these differences in rank (which we shall denote by Σd^2) is then used in the calculation of r according to the formula (to be proved presently) :

$$r = 1 - \frac{6\Sigma d^2}{N(N^2 - 1)}$$

where, as hitherto, there are N pairs of observations. This is an exact formula for the coefficient of correlation between the *ranks*, and the approximation occurs in taking the correlation between the ranks instead of the correlation between the *original readings*. In general these two coefficients of correlation do not vary by more than $0 \cdot 02$, so that the method of ranks gives a very close approximation.

The proof of the above formula is quite simple. Suppose the ranks corresponding to the two original series are X_1, $X_2 \ldots X_N$ and $Y_1, Y_2 \ldots Y_N$, then each of these series consists of the numbers $1, 2, 3 \ldots N$, but in different orders. Therefore we can obtain simple expressions for the mean and standard deviation of each set as follows :

$$\bar{X} = \frac{1 + 2 + 3 + \ldots + N}{N}$$
$$= \frac{N(N + 1)}{2N} = \frac{N + 1}{2}$$

and since $Y_1, Y_2 \ldots Y_N$ represent the same N numbers (although in different order), $\bar{Y}$ must have the same value.

Again
$$N\sigma_X^2 = \Sigma(X - \bar{X})^2$$
$$= \Sigma X^2 - 2\bar{X}\Sigma X + N\bar{X}^2$$
$$= \Sigma X^2 - 2\bar{X} \cdot N\bar{X} + N\bar{X}^2$$
$$= \Sigma X^2 - N\bar{X}^2$$

Now
$$\Sigma X^2 = 1^2 + 2^2 + 3^2 + \ldots + N^2$$
$$= \frac{N(N + 1)(2N + 1)}{6} \text{ from algebraic theory.}$$

Hence $N\sigma_X^2 = \dfrac{N(N + 1)(2N + 1)}{6} - N \cdot \left(\dfrac{N + 1}{2}\right)^2$
$$= \frac{N(N + 1)(N - 1)}{12}$$

so that $\sigma_X^2 = \dfrac{N^2 - 1}{12}$; and again, since $Y_1, Y_2, \ldots Y_N$ are the same N numbers, σ_Y^2 will have the same value.

The quantity Σd^2 which has to be calculated can be expressed in terms of ΣXY because

$$\Sigma d^2 = \Sigma(X - Y)^2$$
$$= \Sigma X^2 - 2\Sigma XY + \Sigma Y^2$$

As we have seen

$$\Sigma X^2 = \frac{N(N + 1)(2N + 1)}{6} = \Sigma Y^2$$

so that $\Sigma d^2 = \dfrac{2N(N + 1)(2N + 1)}{6} - 2\Sigma XY$

i.e. $\Sigma XY = \dfrac{N(N + 1)(2N + 1)}{6} - \tfrac{1}{2}\Sigma d^2$

Finally, the coefficient of correlation between the two ranks can be expressed by

$$r = \frac{\Sigma XY - N\bar{X}\bar{Y}}{N\sigma_X\sigma_Y}$$

$$= \frac{\frac{N(N+1)(2N+1)}{6} - \frac{1}{2}\Sigma d^2 - N\left(\frac{N+1}{2}\right)^2}{\frac{N \cdot (N^2 - 1)}{12}}$$

$$= 1 - \frac{6\Sigma d^2}{N(N^2 - 1)}$$

the formula we have quoted.

Example : Consider the example chosen at the beginning of this chapter, viz. that dealing with the number of wide shots out of ten, and the number of minutes run at the double, and draw up a table of the ranking in each case, starting from the lowest to the highest.

No. of wide shots out of 10	No. of min. at the double	Rank of wide shots	Rank of min. run	Change in rank (d)
0	0	1	1	0
2	1	2	2	0
5	2	4	3	1
4	3	3	4	1
6	4	5	5	0
8	5	7	6	1
7	6	6	7	1

A further column is required giving the " change in rank " squared and the sum of this column is Σd^2. In this example $\Sigma d^2 = 4$ and $N = 7$, so that

$$r = 1 - \frac{6\Sigma d^2}{N(N^2 - 1)}$$

$$= 1 - \frac{6 \times 4}{7 \times 48}$$

$$= \tfrac{13}{14} = 0.93$$

the same value as that obtained by the ordinary method.

Students should be reminded of the difficulty experienced in ranking if, in the original set, one or more of the values is repeated. This is overcome by assigning a rank equal to the average of the number of places filled. For example, the ranking for a set of numbers 10, 9, 9, 8 would be 1, $2\frac{1}{2}$, $2\frac{1}{2}$, 4, because the two nines fill up the second and third place so that a rank of $2\frac{1}{2}$ is given to each. Again, the set 10, 8, 7, 7, 7, 4 would be ranked 1, 2, 4, 4, 4, 6 because the three sevens fill up the third, fourth, and fifth places, so that the rank 4 is assigned to each. This is illustrated in the next example.

Example : Ten pupils are given two tests, and marks are awarded as follows :

Test (A)	10	9	8	8	7	6	6	6	5	5
Test (B)	8	10	8	9	6	7	6	4	5	7

It is required to find the correlation coefficient between the ranks for these two tests.

The work is best set out in columns, thus :

Mark Test (A)	Mark Test (B)	Rank (A)	Rank (B)	Change in Rank	(Change in Rank)²
10	8	1	$3\frac{1}{2}$	$2\frac{1}{2}$	6·25
9	10	2	1	1	1
8	8	$3\frac{1}{2}$	$3\frac{1}{2}$	0	0
8	9	$3\frac{1}{2}$	2	$1\frac{1}{2}$	2·25
7	6	5	$7\frac{1}{2}$	$2\frac{1}{2}$	6·25
6	7	7	$5\frac{1}{2}$	$1\frac{1}{2}$	2·25
6	6	7	$7\frac{1}{2}$	$\frac{1}{2}$	·25
6	4	7	10	3	9
5	5	$9\frac{1}{2}$	9	$\frac{1}{2}$	·25
5	7	$9\frac{1}{2}$	$5\frac{1}{2}$	4	16

43·50

The sum of the last column gives Σd^2, the sum of the squares of the changes in rank. Thus in this case $\Sigma d^2 = 43\frac{1}{2}$, $N = 10$, so that

$$r = 1 - \frac{6\Sigma d^2}{N(N^2 - 1)}$$

$$= 1 - \frac{6(43\frac{1}{2})}{10(99)}$$

$$= 0 \cdot 74$$

The true correlation coefficient between the original marks for the two tests is $0 \cdot 72$. This should be verified by the student.

USE OF CORRELATION COEFFICIENT IN DETERMINING LAG

Suppose we are given the problem of finding if there is any correlation between the two following sets of numbers representing the values of two variables taken at fifteen successive intervals of time.

Interval	1	2	3	4	5	6	7	8	9	10	11	12	13	14	15
Variable (A)	10	11	15	8	5	9	26	30	32	20	22	27	25	0	6
Variable (B)	10	9	12	13	14	18	7	8	11	26	28	29	16	19	23

Now it is a comparatively difficult matter to look at two rows of figures and decide correctly to what extent there is any correlation, and in this case especially there appears to be no connection. The correlation coefficient between A and B may be calculated in this case as it stands, and it will be found to be approximately $- 0 \cdot 2$, indicating no reliable correlation, but it must be always borne in mind when dealing with variables taken at intervals of time that there may be a time-effect operating, *i.e.* the effect of variables A on variables B may only occur after a certain period of time. It is thus very possible that there may be a considerable degree of correlation between the two variables, once a time-lag has been allowed for.

The first step in the consideration of such a lag should be

the drawing of a graph of the two variables. The graph of the above figures is given below :

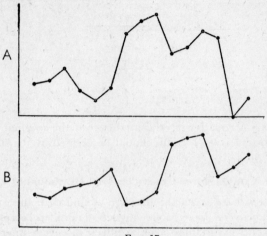

Fig. 17

From these graphs it is immediately apparent that the chart of B follows the shape of the chart of A, but at a little later stage, in this case, about three intervals of time. Certainty about the amount of lag and the then degree of correlation, especially in less well-defined cases, can only be obtained by working out the correlation coefficients between the two sets for varying amounts of lag.

These results in our example are as follows :

Amount of lag (in time intervals)	Correlation coefficient
0	− 0·2
1	0·1
2	0·64
3	0·98
4	0·53
5	0·01

It thus becomes clear that there is a very high degree of correlation when the items of variable A are correlated with the items of variable B three intervals later, *i.e.* there is a time-lag of three intervals, and then there is almost perfect correlation.

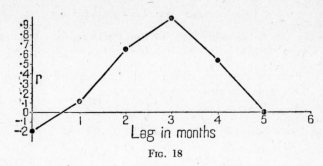

FIG. 18

EXERCISE B

1. The marks obtained by 10 students in two examinations, Pure Mathematics and Applied Mathematics, are given in the following percentages :

	1	2	3	4	5	6	7	8	9	10
Pure Maths.	98	92	88	85	76	72	64	57	48	22
Applied Maths.	84	95	98	87	78	70	75	60	63	45

Find the coefficient of correlation between the ranks in this case.

2. The following figures give the capital employed by a firm in ten successive years together with the profit made in each year, both in hundreds of pounds. :

Capital	10	20	30	40	50	60	70	80	90	100
Profit	2	4	8	5	10	15	14	20	22	30

Find the true correlation coefficient and the correlation coefficient between the ranks.

3. The figures below give the number of criminal convictions (in thousands) and the numbers unemployed (in millions) for the years 1924 to 1933. Use the method of ranks to find the correlation between them.

	1924	1925	1926	1927	1928	1929	1930	1931	1932	1933
No. convicted of crime	7·88	8·12	7·86	7·25	7·44	7·22	8·28	8·83	10·54	9·46
No. unemployed	1·26	1·24	1·43	1·19	1·33	1·34	2·5	2·67	2·78	2·26

4. Ten students were examined in Mathematics and in Physics. Their percentage marks were as follows :

	1	2	3	4	5	6	7	8	9	10
Maths.	78	36	98	25	75	82	90	62	65	39
Physics	84	51	91	60	68	62	86	58	53	47

Find the true and rank correlation coefficients.

CHAPTER IX

ELEMENTARY IDEAS IN PROBABILITY

THE word " probability " is used in ordinary speech to reflect a sense of expectation as when we say, " It will probably rain." This means that on previous occasions when the signs have been the same as those seen at present, rain has in fact followed, and so we are reading the outcome in the future from our experience in the past. When we come to a mathematical treatment of probability it is precisely with this that we are always faced. We have a certain amount of information of a limited nature. In itself it does not amount to a certainty ; if it did we could say positively what would happen. It does not, and so we express it as a probability, more or less strong. A very high probability, we would say, is very close to certainty ; a very low probability is very close to impossibility. Between these two extremes lies uncertainty in varying degrees. We illustrate this in the following way.

A platoon of soldiers is seen marching into a wood. If all exits of the wood are under observation and none are seen leaving we are certain they are still there after a certain time. If they have been seen leaving it is impossible that they could be there. If all exits to the wood are not under observation it is uncertain, and there will be some degree of probability that they are still there.

Our problem in this chapter is to try to make definite and calculable the idea and practice of probability, for its importance lies not simply in the fact that it bridges the gap between certainty and impossibility as an idea, but because it has a definite importance in practice. Let us illustrate this : Fuses are being turned out to a standard form by a machine. To reach the requisite standard they must pass between two gauges set to an upper and lower limit. A hundred of these fuses are chosen at random, and it is found that 10 of them cannot pass the gauge test. Another batch of 100 is taken, and 5 fail to pass the test. If a consignment of 1,000 fuses is taken, what is the most probable number of fuses that will fail to pass the test? More definitely, what is the probability that out of 1,000, 80 will fail? These are questions of obvious importance in production, but they have a still wider importance. If, for example, out of 100 recruits sent through a training course, 10 fail to pass the final test, and if out of the next batch 5 fail to pass, what is the most probable number to be expected as failures in the next batch? If you are sent through the course, what is *your* probability of getting through? Clearly an examination of such questions in itself becomes important in the understanding of whether the course is properly adapted to the requirements of the recruits, just as in the previous case an examination of these questions will enable us to decide whether the method of production is in fact properly standardized.

What has to be examined is whether the variations which occur are " reasonable " variations, allowing for small accidents, or whether there is something systematically wrong with the scheme of production.

Our first step, therefore, is to state clearly what we take as a measure of probability. We begin with an example.

Example 1 : In a batch of 100 men it is found that 12 of them wear glasses. We say that $\frac{12}{100}$ is the probability that a man in that batch wears glasses. It is, of course, the fraction of men who do wear glasses, but this fraction is regarded as a characteristic of the 100 men as a whole, and in a certain sense of every member of that 100. The sense in which it is so used could be seen in this way. If only the names of the men appeared on a list, then one would say that any particular one (Tom Jones, for example) has a probability of $\frac{12}{100}$ of wearing glasses. This seems a peculiar method of determining whether Tom Jones wears glasses, but for purposes of probability he has to be regarded as a typical member of a composite group.

Example 2 : Suppose 12 wear glasses, and 8 require glasses but do not wear them, then we would say that the probability of Tom Jones (whom we know only by name) wearing glasses is $\frac{12}{100}$, while the probability that he requires glasses but is not wearing them is $\frac{8}{100}$. Both probabilities can be attached to Tom Jones.

Example 3 : We notice that there are 80 men who neither wear glasses nor need them. We can, therefore, attach a third probability to Tom Jones, namely $\frac{80}{100}$, that he neither wears glasses nor requires them. In such a group, therefore, every member has attached to him a whole series of probabilities of this nature.

Note : There are the three possibilities ; Tom Jones wears glasses, Tom Jones does not wear glasses but requires them, Tom Jones does not wear glasses and does not need them. It is *certain* that Tom Jones belongs to one of these groups. We notice that the sum of the three probabilities attached to Tom Jones, namely, $\frac{12}{100} + \frac{8}{100} + \frac{80}{100} = \frac{100}{100} = 1$. We are led, therefore, to see that certainty corresponds to a value of the probability equal to 1. Moreover, had the number of recruits wearing glasses been zero, *i.e.* had no-one worn glasses, the probability of Tom Jones wearing glasses would have been $\frac{0}{100} = 0$; or, if we care, we can say that it is *certain* that the assertion that Tom Jones wears glasses is false. Summing up, therefore, we have the three cases :

Probability $= 1$ means certainty
Probability $= 0$ means impossibility or falsehood
Uncertainty (or all other probabilities) lies between 0 and 1

It is usual to write p for the probability, so that p will lie between 0 and 1

Addition Rule for Probability

It should be easy to understand the following general argument. Let m be the number of recruits wearing glasses, n be the number of recruits who need glasses but do not wear them, and r the number who neither wear them nor need them. Thus the total number of recruits is $m + n + r$. Then the probability that a man wears glasses is $\dfrac{m}{m + n + r} = p_1$, say. The probability that he needs glasses but does not wear them is $\dfrac{n}{m + n + r} = p_2$, say. The probability that he neither wears them nor needs them is $\dfrac{r}{m + n + r} = p_3$, say. Then the probability that a man belongs *either* to the first *or* second group is

$$\frac{m}{m + n + r} + \frac{n}{m + n + r} = \frac{m + n}{m + n + r} = p_1 + p_2$$

Note also the probability that he belongs neither to the first nor the second is

$$\frac{r}{m + n + r} = \frac{(m + n + r) - (m + n)}{m + n + r}$$
$$= 1 - (p_1 + p_2) = p_3$$

and this of course also follows from the fact that $p_1 + p_2 + p_3 = 1$.

Multiplication Law

Out of 100 recruits 12 wear glasses and 15 have artificial teeth. The probability that Tom Jones wears glasses is $\frac{12}{100}$. The probability that Tom Jones has artificial teeth is $\frac{15}{100}$. What is the probability that Tom Jones wears glasses *and* has artificial teeth ? (*Note*: In the Addition Rule we had *either — or*, but here we have *and*. This is commonly called a double event.)

The recruits can be classified in four ways :

   (*a*) Those who have neither false teeth nor glasses.
   (*b*) Those who have no false teeth but wear glasses.
   (*c*) Those who have false teeth but wear no glasses.
   (*d*) Those who have false teeth and wear glasses.

If it is possible for every recruit to belong to any one of these classifications how many possibilities are there ?

We can imagine the recruits lined up twice such that :

   (i) In the first line the first 12 recruits wear glasses, while the remaining 88 are without glasses.

  (ii) In the second line the first 15 recruits have false teeth while the remaining 85 have none.

Now any particular recruit, if we know nothing about him beyond the fact that he is a recruit, may be any one of the first hundred, and also any one of the second hundred. There are therefore 100×100 possibilities altogether.

How many will show the characteristics glasses *and* false teeth as possibilities in this way ?

There are 12 in the first row and each of these 12 may be associated with any one of the 15 in the second row. There are thus 12×15 combined possibilities altogether.

Thus the ratio of all the possibilities of " glasses *and* artificial teeth " to all the possibilities without restriction is

$$(12 \times 15)/(100 \times 100)$$

and this on the basis of our original definition of probability gives the probability of the double event. We note that

$$\frac{12 \times 15}{100 \times 100} = \frac{12}{100} \times \frac{15}{100}$$

= product of the separate probabilities.

This is evidently true in general. If p_1 and p_2 are two independent probabilities applicable to the same group of size N such that $p_1 = \frac{m}{N}$ and $p_2 = \frac{n}{N}$, then two lines A and B can be supposed divided by N points such that in A there are m and in B there are n, representing the two characteristics to which the probabilities apply. Of the $N \times N$ possible joins of all the pairs of points, one in A to one in B, there are $m \times n$, which correspond to the characteristics occurring together. Thus the probability of the double event is

$$\frac{m \times n}{N \times N} = \frac{m}{N} \times \frac{n}{N} = p_1 \times p_2$$

We conclude, therefore, with the Multiplication Law, viz. that if p_1 and p_2 are the probabilities of two events separately occurring to members of the same group, the probability of both occurring to any member of that group is $p_1 \times p_2$.

BERNOULLI'S LAW

This is a fundamental proposition in probability, but it is best explained by reference to a particular example. Nevertheless the example will be so general as to involve the proof of the theorem itself. Let us suppose that on the basis of past experience it is found that bomb-aimers at a certain stage of their training manage on the average to place a definite proportion of the bombs they drop actually within the target area. The ratio of the successes to the total number of trials can then be taken as a measure of the probability of any individual shot falling within the target area. Let this probability be p. The question we ask is, if a bomb-aimer takes n shots at a target, what is the probability that some number of these, say r, fall within the target area on that occasion? The probability of the first shot being successful is p, and of the first two shots being successful is $p \times p$. Therefore the probability of the first r shots being successful is $p \times p \times p \times \ldots$ to r terms $= p^r$, but since we are concerned with precisely r and no more successes on this basis, every other shot must fail; thus the probability of the $(r + 1)$th shot failing is $(1 - p)$ and of the $(r + 1)$th and the $(r + 2)$th shots failing is $(1 - p)(1 - p)$, i.e. $(1 - p)^2$. It is easily seen, therefore, that the probability of the first r shots succeeding and the remaining $n - r$ shots failing is $p^r(1 - p)^{n-r}$.

Is this the answer to our problem? No. We did not ask what the probability is of the *first* r shots succeeding and the remainder failing; we asked simply that any r shots should succeed and the remainder fail. There is obviously a much greater probability of this occurring than of the case we have calculated; we have, in fact, to add to that already calculated the probability of all the other possible arrangements of shots, r of which are successful, among n. In how many ways can r places for the order of the successful shots be found among n total possibilities? The answer is simply the ways in which a group of r things can be formed from any n objects, viz.

$$\frac{n(n-1)(n-2) \ldots (n-r+1)}{1.2.3 \ldots r} = \frac{n!}{r!\,(n-r)!}$$

This number has to be multiplied by $p^r(1-p)^{n-r}$; hence we conclude that the probability of exactly r successes in n trials on a given occasion is $\frac{n!}{r!(n-r)!}\,p^r(1-p)^{n-r}$. This is known as Bernoulli's Theorem.

Example 1 : What is the probability that when five pennies are tossed, three will turn up heads?

The probability of a penny turning up heads can be taken as $\frac{1}{2}$. The total number of tossings is 5. Thus $n = 5$. The number of successes required is 3, *i.e.* $r = 3$. Hence probability required is

$$\frac{5!}{3!\ 2!}\,(\tfrac{1}{2})^3\,(1-\tfrac{1}{2})^2 = \frac{5.4.3.2.1}{3.2.1.2.1}\,(\tfrac{1}{2})^5 = \tfrac{5}{16}$$

Example 2 : Suppose an event is successful on the average on one occasion in every n trials. The probability of a successful event is $\frac{1}{n}$. The probability that the event will fail (not be successful) is $1 - \frac{1}{n}$. We inquire what the probability is that

out of the next n shots, all will fail. Here, then, $p = 1 - \frac{1}{n}$, $r = n$.
Hence by Bernoulli's Theorem the required probability is

$$= \frac{n!}{r! \, (n - r)!} \, p^r (1 - p)^{n-r}$$

$$= \frac{n!}{n! \, o!} \left(1 - \frac{1}{n}\right)^n \left(\frac{1}{n}\right)^o$$

$$= \left(1 - \frac{1}{n}\right)^n$$

a result which could have been derived by direct use of the Multiplication Theorem, since the event with probability $1 - \frac{1}{n}$ has to occur n times in succession. The result has a special significance when n is large, for in that case if we expand $\left(1 - \frac{1}{n}\right)$ by the Binomial theorem, we obtain

$$1 + n\left(-\frac{1}{n}\right) + \frac{n(n-1)}{2!}\left(-\frac{1}{n}\right)^2 + \frac{n(n-1)\,(n-2)}{3!}\left(-\frac{1}{n}\right)^3 + \ldots$$

$$= 1 - \frac{1}{1!} + \frac{1}{2!}\left(1 - \frac{1}{n}\right) - \frac{1}{3!}\left(1 - \frac{1}{n}\right)\left(1 - \frac{2}{n}\right) + \ldots$$

and if n is regarded as so large that the terms $\frac{1}{n}, \frac{2}{n} \ldots$ may be finally ignored without affecting this sum, we obtain the series

$$1 - \frac{1}{1!} + \frac{1}{2!} - \frac{1}{3!} + \ldots$$

This is an important series, and is a particular case of the " *exponential* " series. The series $1 + \frac{1}{1!} + \frac{1}{2!} + \frac{1}{3!} + \ldots$ has the numerical value 2·71828 . . . and is usually referred to as e. The series $1 + \dfrac{x}{1!} + \dfrac{x^2}{2!} + \dfrac{x^3}{3!} + \ldots$ can be shown to be e^x.

When $x = -1$ we have the series obtained above, so that

$$1 - \frac{1}{1!} + \frac{1}{2!} - \frac{1}{3!} + \ldots = e^{-1} = \frac{1}{e}$$

We can state, therefore, that if a rare event occurs once in n trials, the probability that it will fail on n successive occasions is e^{-1}.

Example 3 : We can generalize this by inquiring : If a rare event occurs once in n trials, what is the probability that it will not occur on m successive occasions ? In this case the required probability is clearly $\left(1 - \dfrac{1}{n}\right)^m = \left(1 - \dfrac{1}{n}\right)^{n.\frac{m}{n}}$ We have just seen that when n is large $\left(1 - \dfrac{1}{n}\right)^n$ approaches e^{-1}. Thus the required probability approaches $e^{-\frac{m}{n}}$.

Example 4 : We can state this proposition in a slightly modified form. If the n events are regarded as spaced throughout an interval of time, say t sec., and m events throughout an interval of time T sec., then $e^{-\frac{T}{t}}$ is the probability that if an event occurs on the average once in t sec. it will not occur during a period of time T sec.

Geometrical Probability

We can apply the simple ideas of probability to the treatment of problems that can be re-stated in geometrical form.

Example : Supposing it is known that a certain target occupies half an acre within a wider area of 5 acres, but that the actual location within the wider area is not known, then it is clear that if bombing is to take place, it is the wider area that has to be attacked in the hope that the target be reached. If any shot falls within the wider area, then it is obvious that the probability of hitting the target is $\frac{1}{2}/5 = \frac{1}{10}$. In this case we merely take the ratio of the two areas as the probability. The same type of problem arises when it is known that the explosion of a bomb will damage everything within a certain given radius, then the probability that damage will accrue to a target of small area within the area in which the bomb falls will be the ratio of the range of damage of the bomb divided by the target area, provided the former lies entirely within the latter.

Example : Suppose it be known that on the average 1 in 3 bombs fall within a given target area of size $\frac{1}{2}$ acre and that the actual target in this area itself occupies $\frac{1}{10}$ acre, then the probability of a bomb falling within the target area is $\frac{1}{3}$, the probability that if a bomb falls within the target area it strikes the actual target is $\frac{\frac{1}{10}}{\frac{1}{2}}$. Hence the probability that a particular bomb will strike the target is $\frac{1}{3} \times \frac{1}{10}/\frac{1}{2}$, *i.e.* $\frac{1}{3} \times \frac{2}{10} = \frac{1}{15}$.

FURTHER REMARKS ON THE MEANING OF PROBABILITY

In the foregoing discussion we have supposed that it is possible to give a definite value to the probability of the occurrence of the kinds of events under consideration. We have said, for example, that the probability of a head appearing when a coin is tossed is $\frac{1}{2}$. If we base this on the fact that there are only two possibilities, head and tail, and that they are equally likely to appear, or that their probabilities are equal, then, of course, we must say that the value of p is $\frac{1}{2}$. But if we examine the statement we have just made its meaning in practice is that if we keep on tossing such a coin we shall find that after a sufficient number of tossings there will be an equal number of heads and tails. Or we might say that the difference between the heads and tails in number will become progressively a smaller and smaller fraction of the whole. What is the evidence for this ? And if it is based on experimental evidence of this nature we are being driven to take rather a different view from that presented in the first instance. Let us contrast two statements that sum up these viewpoints :

(i) The probability is $\frac{1}{2}$, because there are only two possibilities with nothing to distinguish between them, and one of them must always occur.

(ii) The probability is $\frac{1}{2}$, because it is found that the ratio of the number of heads to the total number of tossings gets nearer and nearer to $\frac{1}{2}$ as the number of tossings increases.

The first statement gives a mathematical definition, the second an experimental definition. The theory we have developed has been based on the assumption that a definite value of p, the probability, actually exists, and in itself has not depended on any experimental verifications of the results. Indeed the difficulties in verifying such results are apparent as soon as one looks carefully at the second statement, which depends on the most elementary notion. If after tossing a penny for a large number of times, we decide that after another hundred tossings we will have done enough, it *might* turn out that practically the whole of these hundred give heads. The result might be that at the end of our experiment we are further away from p equal to $\frac{1}{2}$ than we were at an earlier stage. Are we then to say that we still have not gone far enough ? What in fact is meant experimentally by the statement that p gets nearer and nearer to $\frac{1}{2}$ as the number of tossings is increased ? We evidently cannot say that " after a certain number of tossings " this is bound to happen, because it is not the case. And yet there is no escaping the fact that p equal to $\frac{1}{2}$ is what we are bound to expect.

To overcome difficulties such as these we approach the subject in this way. We do not in the first instance think of any experiment at all to test our assumptions. We begin merely by setting out all the possible *imagined* arrangements that can be thought of. We set out all the possible imagined arrangements that correspond to success. The ratio of the latter to the former is what we have defined as our probability. We assume that in an idealized experiment, that is, one we can conceive of, all these possibilities occur with their corresponding frequency. We can then raise a direct question in any actual experiment, viz. How far does any given experiment agree with this idealized one? If we say that the idealized experiment represents the operation of chance since every possibility is allowed for, our question then simply resolves itself into the more definite question, How far can the results of any given actual experiment be accounted for by chance? If it can be accounted for in this way, we would say the result of the experiment was not significant. Otherwise we would be bound to agree that something other than chance was in operation. Let us illustrate this with a simple example.

An individual is firing at a horizontal line. He fires ten shots of which nine fall above the line and one below. Is there something significant about this?

When we pose this question what we are really asking is, "Could this have occurred by chance?" The answer is, of course, "Yes—but it is not very likely." What we want to know is exactly how likely it is. We assume that *by chance* means that in the idealized chance experiment a shot is just as likely to lie above as below the line; that in fact the probability of a shot lying above the line in any single case is $\frac{1}{2}$.

If, therefore, p is $\frac{1}{2}$, what is the probability that in ten trials nine will lie above, or in the present sense be successful? This involves a direct application of Bernoulli's Theorem.

We have $\qquad p = \frac{1}{2},\ n = 10,\ r = 9$

Thus $\qquad \begin{aligned} P &= \frac{n!}{r!\,(n-r)!}\ p^r (1-p)^{n-r} \\[4pt] &= \frac{10!}{9!\ 1!}\ \frac{1}{2^{10}} \\[4pt] &= \tfrac{5}{512} \end{aligned}$

Thus we find that in such an experiment we might expect that nine shots out of ten would fall above the line in 5 tests out of 512, or roughly in one test in a hundred.

Is nine shots out of ten above the line significant? The answer is in terms of another question. Can we expect this to be the one test out of a hundred? We look at the conditions under which the marksman carried through the shootings, and we can safely decide that to account for his results by chance is too far-fetched. His results are, therefore, significant, in the sense that there is something significant about his marksmanship.

By means of the mathematical theory of probability, therefore, we are enabled to set up a *standard of chance* against which we can gauge whether the results of an experiment can be attributed to chance effects or whether there is something really significant in operation.

It is not difficult to see the next step, and again we can illustrate by means of a particular example. Suppose the marksman were required to fire, not at a line but at the space or interval between two horizontal lines. As a gauge or standard against which to measure the significance of any particular test we would require to set up the idealized experiment in which the idealized marksman is thought of as firing at the line lying midway between the two given lines. We can now no longer work on the simple assumption that the probability of a shot falling above the line is equal to that of one falling below the line. We require an idealized case in which we can find the probability of a shot falling wide of the line by some given amount. It is clear enough that the probability must be small that the shot will fall very wide of the central line, and large that it will fall close to that line. This says that the chance of a shot lying close to the central line is large, but that this chance falls off as the distance from the line increases. Thus the probability of a shot falling anywhere will depend on the distance of this position from the central line. The probability in fact in the idealized case is now no longer a fixed constant ($\frac{1}{2}$ in the previous example), but is a function of the deviation from the central line. When we have discovered what this is in the idealized experiment we should then be in a position to calculate the probability of a shot falling within the region bounded by any two parallel lines. This problem will be dealt with in Chapter XII, where we set up the Gaussian Law of Error, which is simply the law that replaces p equal to $\frac{1}{2}$ in the simple case we have dealt with in this chapter.

EXERCISES

1. Two men are selected from a group of ten men, among whom are two brothers. What is the probability that the two brothers will be selected ?

2. Ten men, among whom are two brothers, stand in single file. What is the probability that the two brothers will be standing next to each other ?

3. Five men sit down to dinner at a round table. What is the probability that a certain pair will not be next to each other ?

4. What is the probability of a penny showing at least one head when tossed 5 times ?

5. What is the probability of all the 13 cards in a hand of bridge being (i) red, (ii) black, (iii) all of one colour ?

6. What is the probability of drawing two aces in succession from a pack of 52 cards if (i) the first ace is returned to the pack, (ii) the first ace is not returned to the pack ?

7. What is the probability that a hand of 13 cards from a pack of 52 cards shall contain (i) exactly 3 black cards, (ii) exactly 6 red cards, (iii) exactly 7 red cards and the two black aces ?

8. A sniper kills once in four shots on the average. What is the probability that he will miss on five successive occasions ?

9. A coin is tossed ten times. Show that the probability of at least six heads appearing in succession is $\frac{5}{64}$.

10. If on the average a certain type of aeroplane flies 2,500 miles without mishap, what is the probability that a particular aeroplane of this type will fly 5,000 miles without mishap ?

11. If a dice is thrown, what is the probability of not getting a six in the first six throws?

12. If on the average it rains 10 days out of the 30 in a certain month, what is the probability that on ten successive days it will not rain?

13. Given the two sets of numbers, 1, 2, 3, 4, 5 ; 2, 4, 6, 8, 10, what is the probability that the sum of two numbers selected, one from each group, will have 11 as their sum?
Write down the probability of the occurrence of every number between 3 and 15.
What is the probability of getting an odd number?

14. Three men agree to meet at the King's Arms tavern in a certain town. There are, however, three such taverns. What is the probability that they will (i) all come to the same tavern, (ii) all go to different taverns?

15. It is known that three groups of snipers may each consist of 1, 2, or 3 men. What is the probability that the total number of snipers is 6?
What is the probability that the total number does not exceed 6?

16. What is the probability of throwing not more than 4 with three dice?

17. What is the probability of throwing not more than 5 with three dice?

18. A marksman fires at a horizontal rope held taut. Out of 12 shots, 10 pass below the rope and 2 above. Show that the probability that this apparent bias might occur by chance is approximately $\frac{1}{64}$.

19. Two balls are drawn from a bag containing 5 red and 7 white balls. Find the chance that they will both be white.

20. Three balls are to be drawn from a bag containing 2 black, 2 white, and 2 red balls. Show that the odds are 3 to 2 against drawing a ball of each colour, and 4 to 1 against drawing 2 white balls.

21. A party of n persons take their seats at random at a round table. Show that it is $(n - 3)$ to 2 against two specified persons sitting together.

22. Find the probability of throwing one six at least in 6 throws with a dice.

23. Find the chance of throwing 8 with two dice.

24. Three cards are drawn at random from an ordinary pack. Find the chance that they will consist of a knave, a king, and a queen.

25. Six men occupying six bunks in a room return together at night fuddled with alcohol and enter any bunk that is vacant. What is the probability that each will sleep in his own bunk ? What is the probability that at least two will sleep in their correct bunks ?

CHAPTER X

THE MEANING OF THE CORRELATION COEFFICIENT

IN this chapter we propose to dig a little deeper into the meaning of the correlation coefficient than we have hitherto done. So far it has arisen merely as a measure of a trend, or of a causal relation that was known to exist, between two varying quantities.

Can we reverse the statement? Can we say that if a correlation coefficient of, say, 0·7 or 0·9 is found between two varying quantities, that, to some degree, the one is the cause of the other, or that it is one of the causes that determines the other?

It is clear enough that we cannot say this. The amount of money a group of people may have in their pockets, for example, may fall steadily from a greatest value at the beginning of the week to its smallest value at the end of the week before the next wages are due. It may also be the case that the output of work per head may likewise fall off from its greatest value at the beginning of the week to its lowest ebb at the end. The correlation between these two may therefore be very high, but there is little reason to suppose that this measures the extent to which the one is a cause of the other.

The correlation coefficient, moreover, does not give any indication regarding which is to be seen as cause and which as effect. This in itself, however, is not a disadvantage, for, after all, both may be effects of common causes, and as we shall see in a moment, when there are causes in common between two effects, we must expect some measure of correlation between them. Summing up, then, we can say that a correlation coefficient can have a meaning for us only when there lies at the back of it all some reason for supposing that the two quantities that do so correlate are linked in some causal way. Naturally, of course, in practice this is the case, for one does not set out to measure a correlation unless one suspects just some such linkage between the two factors involved. In itself, however, the existence of a correlation coefficient, whatever its magnitude, need signify nothing.

When such a causal relation is known to exist, it is not difficult to see in what way the coefficient becomes a measure, and of what it is a measure in certain simple cases.

Suppose there are three sets of n numbers :

$$a_1, \quad a_2, \quad a_3, \quad a_4, \quad \ldots \; a_n$$
$$b_1, \quad b_2, \quad b_3, \quad b_4, \quad \ldots \; b_n$$
$$c_1, \quad c_2, \quad c_3, \quad c_4, \quad \ldots \; c_n$$

We shall assume that these are all deviations from the same average, say 0, with the same standard deviation σ. Thus

$$n\sigma^2 = \Sigma a^2 = \Sigma b^2 = \Sigma c^2$$

Also suppose there is no correlation between the three sets of numbers, so that the numerator in each expression for r must be zero. Hence

$$\Sigma ab = 0, \quad \Sigma bc = 0, \quad \Sigma ca = 0$$

We propose now to build up two other sets of numbers from these, say X and Y,

(1) By adding the a's, b's, and c's together, viz.

$$X_1 = a_1 + b_1 + c_1 \qquad \qquad X_2 = a_2 + b_2 + c_2$$
$$X_3 = a_3 + b_3 + c_3, \ldots$$

(2) By adding only the b's and c's together, viz.

$$Y_1 = b_1 + c_1 \quad Y_2 = b_2 + c_2 \quad Y_3 = b_3 + c_3 \ldots$$

In a sense we can say that the numbers X and Y have two out of three separate causes in common. What correlation, if any, exists between the X's and the Y's ?

Since the averages of the a's, b's, and c's are 0, so also are the averages of the X's and the Y's.

Thus, if r is the required correlation coefficient

$$r^2 = \frac{[\Sigma XY]^2}{\Sigma X^2 \Sigma Y^2} = \frac{[\Sigma(a+b+c)(b+c)]^2}{\Sigma(a+b+c)^2 \Sigma(b+c^2)}$$

Since $(a+b+c)(b+c) = ab + ac + 2bc + b^2 + c^2$

and $\Sigma ab = 0, \Sigma ac = 0, \Sigma bc = 0, \Sigma b^2 = n\sigma^2 = \Sigma c^2$

therefore $\Sigma(a+b+c)(b+c) = 2n\sigma^2$

Also, in the same way

$$\Sigma(a+b+c)^2 = 3n\sigma^2, \quad \Sigma(b+c)^2 = 2n\sigma^2$$

Thus $r^2 = \dfrac{(2n\sigma^2)^2}{3n\sigma^2 . 2n\sigma^2} = \dfrac{4n^2\sigma^4}{6n^2\sigma^4} = \dfrac{2}{3}$

Thus in this case it is seen that r^2, the square of the correlation coefficient, is a measure of the proportion of causes common to the two quantities X and Y whose correlation coefficient is given by r. This result can clearly be generalized to cover the case of m causes in common out of a total n. When this proportion is 1, so that both are uniquely determined by the same causes, $r = 1$. When $r = 0$ there are no causal factors in common, and the two quantities are quite independent.

How is the correlation coefficient affected by the number of pairs of values in any correlation table?

If there are only two pairs, then clearly there are only two points on the diagram for the lines of regression, and they fix it uniquely ; the two lines of regression fall together and the correlation coefficient must be 1.

Exercise : Verify by calculation that if $x = a$ and b, when $y = $ A and B respectively, then the correlation coefficient is 1.

Suppose now that there are three pairs of corresponding values, and for simplicity let $x = 1, 2,$ and 3, while y also adopts these values but not necessarily in that order.

What are the various values of the correlation coefficient that can be obtained ? The table of values of x and y would run separately like this :

x	y	x	y	x	y	x	y	x	y	x	y
1	1	1	1	1	2	1	2	1	3	1	3
2	2	2	3	2	3	2	1	2	1	2	2
3	3	3	2	3	1	3	3	3	2	3	1

From an examination of these six tables we can obtain all the possible correlation coefficients. Let us find them. The average $\bar{x}$ is 2 and the average $\bar{y}$ is 2. Hence the tables of deviations are :

X	Y	X	Y	X	Y	X	Y	X	Y	X	Y
-1	-1	-1	-1	-1	0	-1	0	-1	1	-1	1
0	0	0	1	0	1	0	-1	0	-1	0	0
1	1	1	0	1	-1	1	1	1	0	1	-1

Remembering that in each case

$$\Sigma X^2 = 2 \text{ and } \Sigma Y^2 = 2, \text{ and } r = \Sigma XY / \sqrt{(\Sigma X^2 . \Sigma Y^2)}$$

we easily find the following values for r :

$$1, \ 0.5, \ -0.5, \ 0.5, \ -0.5, \ -1.$$

In 1 case in 6 the value of r is   1
,, 2 cases ,, 6 ,,   ,,   0.5
,, 2 ,, ,, 6 ,,   ,, -0.5
,, 1 case ,, 6 ,,   ,, -1

Now let us imagine that an experiment has been conducted or data have been collected in such circumstances that the values of x and of y had to be 1, 2, or 3, and for the present purpose none of these numbers could be repeated in the table. Then the actual set found would have to be one of the set of six tables given above.

Suppose it were the second, viz.

$$x \quad 1 \quad 2 \quad 3$$
$$y \quad 1 \quad 3 \quad 2$$

On working out the correlation between x and y, one finds, of course, that $r = 0 \cdot 5$.

How much weight or *significance* can we attach to this value ? We notice that if we had taken all the possible arrangements indiscriminately we would have obtained $0 \cdot 5$ in 2 cases out of 6. Stated otherwise this says that the probability of obtaining $0 \cdot 5$ *by chance* is 1 in 3, quite a high probability.

If, therefore, $r = 0 \cdot 5$ could have been obtained so easily by chance, it cannot be argued that in this case $r = 0 \cdot 5$ indicates a significant correlation between x and y.

It is usual to consider any correlation coefficient as being without significance if it could have been obtained by chance in at least 1 case in 10.

Exercise : If the three x's must be 1, 2, or 3, and all different, but the three y's may be repeated, but must in each case be 1, 2, or 3, show that the probability of getting $r = 1$ in any given case is $\frac{1}{27}$.

From what we have just seen it is clear that the weight to be attached to a correlation coefficient has to be viewed in the light of the question, " What is the probability that with such a set of data a correlation coefficient of this magnitude might have occurred by chance, and might therefore be spurious ? "

Actually this becomes a problem, when stated in concise terms, capable of being examined mathematically in a way rather similar to the way we have dealt with the illustration. We shall not attempt the mathematical investigation in this book but merely tabulate the result found.

The probability that a set of n pairs of readings will show a correlation of amount r merely by chance will depend both on n and on r. Here, then, is a table showing some of the results of the mathematical investigation referred to :

Pairs of Observations	P = Probability of correlation being accidental			
	P = 0·1	P = 0·05	P = 0·02	P = 0·01
n = 10	r = 0·55	r = 0·63	r = 0·72	r = 0·76
15	0·44	0·51	0·59	0·64
20	0·38	0·44	0·52	0·56
27	0·32	0·38	0·45	0·49
32	0·30	0·35	0·41	0·45
37	0·28	0·32	0·38	0·42
42	0·26	0·30	0·36	0·39
50	0·23	0·28	0·33	0·35
60	0·21	0·25	0·30	0·33
70	0·20	0·23	0·28	0·30
80	0·18	0·22	0·26	0·28
90	0·17	0·20	0·24	0·27
100	0·16	0·20	0·23	0·26

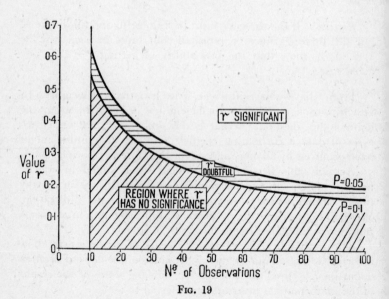

Fig. 19

Example : Suppose 15 pairs of values give a correlation coefficient of 0·60. How significant is this result ?

The second row, for which $n = 15$, gives $r = 0.59$ for P $= 0.02$. A value of $r = 0.60$ would give a slightly smaller value of P.

We may say that this value of r would occur by chance with a probability of 2 in 100 cases or 1 in 50. If 1 in 10 is taken as the significant limiting probability, we can say that in this case the probability that $r = 0.60$ would occur by chance is very slight indeed. This, therefore, would be regarded as a significant correlation.

A safe rule is to say that if P is greater than $\frac{1}{10}$, that is, if the correlation coefficient r could arise by chance in more than 1 case in 10, then r is without significance. If P is less than $\frac{1}{20}$, that is, if r could arise by chance in less than 1 case in 20, then r is taken as definitely significant. If P lies between $\frac{1}{10}$ and $\frac{1}{20}$, *i.e.* between 0·1 and 0·05, the result is regarded as doubtful.

This type of test of significance has already been met in our discussions. It is clear that such tests must play a very important rôle in all statistical analysis. To draw conclusions from data is one thing ; to know the certainty with which these conclusions can be depended on is another. On general grounds we can always say that the greater the amount of data from which conclusions are drawn, the greater the degree of certainty with which these conclusions can be held. The indefinite accumulation of data, however, is clearly impractical ; for one thing, the labour may be prohibitive. On the other hand, there are many circumstances in which judgment has unfortunately to be based on very small samples because these may be all that is available. It is particularly in the case of small samples that tests of significance begin to attain great importance, for it is precisely in such circumstances that dangers arise from samples that are biased. Because a certain penny when tossed four times gave a head on each occasion does not justify us in assuming that if it is tossed on 500 occasions it will give 500 heads. And what is true about the tossing of a penny is equally true about the personal judgments we tend to form on the basis of any very restricted experience.

EXERCISES

1. The following figures give, for 10 students, their age in years and months, and a figure which is a measure of their intelligence :

Student.	1	2	3	4	5	6	7	8	9	10
Age	17 9	18 8	17 0	18 0	17 3	18 11	18 4	18 11	19 8	17 2
Intelligence Quotient .	161	103	168	155	123	141	135	110	134	120

Calculate the coefficient of correlation and examine its significance.

2. The percentage marks obtained by seven pupils in two examinations are given below. Find the true correlation coefficient, the correlation coefficient between the ranks, and examine their significance.

Pupil	1	2	3	4	5	6	7
Exam. (A)	84	75	68	52	46	31	15
Exam. (B)	72	43	84	91	58	28	37

3. Refer to Exercises B (page 97), and in each case examine the significance of the coefficient of correlation.

CHAPTER XI

SOME MATHEMATICAL POINTS

In this chapter we deal with a number of special points of a mathematical nature that we require for the further development of our work. Two remarks are necessary in this connection. In the first place, we do not propose to establish the theorems in any rigorous mathematical sense. We shall state them, and merely give an indication of the nature of the proof, for we are not concerned here with mathematical rigour. In the second place, since the theorems are selected for their use in our later discussion, they will not be connected together logically as one would link up the successive propositions in a subject that is being developed in a mathematical way. They will in fact tend to stand by themselves. This therefore is a chapter of disconnected mathematical points.

(1)

The number normally described as e in mathematical writings is $1 + \frac{1}{1!} + \frac{1}{2!} + \frac{1}{3!} + \frac{1}{4!} + \cdots$. This number is important to us, because, as we shall see, it plays a very important part in connection with statistical distribution and frequency curves. It enters into the expression for the idealized Error Curve, which is used as a standard against which to judge or measure actual errors that arise in experiment. The number e, as we have already seen, is defined as the value of $(1 + 1/n)^n$ when n increases without limit. That this becomes the sum of the series of numbers mentioned above is easily indicated by expanding $(1 + 1/n)^n$ by means of the Binomial Theorem.

Thus $(1 + 1/n)^n =$

$$1 + n\left(\frac{1}{n}\right) + \frac{n(n - 1)}{2!} \frac{1}{n^2} + \frac{n(n - 1)(n - 2)}{3!} \cdot \frac{1}{n^3} + \cdots$$

Now when n becomes exceedingly large

$$\frac{n(n - 1)}{n^2} = \left(1 - \frac{1}{n}\right) \longrightarrow 1$$

$$\frac{n(n - 1)(n - 2)}{n^3} = \left(1 - \frac{1}{n}\right)\left(1 - \frac{2}{n}\right) \longrightarrow 1$$

$$\frac{n(n - 1)(n - 2)(n - 3)}{n^4} = \left(1 - \frac{1}{n}\right)\left(1 - \frac{2}{n}\right)\left(1 - \frac{3}{n}\right) \longrightarrow 1$$

and so on.

Here we have assumed not only that $\frac{1}{n}, \frac{2}{n}, \frac{3}{n}$, etc., each becomes zero, but that the product of the succession of factors, each of which becomes 1, itself also becomes 1. Thus on these assumptions :

$$(1 + 1/n)^n \longrightarrow 1 + \frac{1}{1!} + \frac{1}{2!} + \frac{1}{3!} + \cdots = e$$

when n becomes indefinitely great.

(II)

When n is large, but not indefinitely large, it is possible to estimate e by writing

$$e = (1 + 1/n)^m$$

and choosing a value of m slightly different from n, say,

$$m = n + a$$

where a is small.

Let us write, then, $e = (1 + 1/n)^{n+a}$

or, taking logarithms (to base e) of both sides,

$$1 = (n + a) \log (1 + 1/n)$$

Now it can be shown by algebraic methods that

$$\log (1 + x) = x - \frac{x^2}{2} + \frac{x^3}{3} - \cdots$$

so that $\log (1 + 1/n) = 1/n - 1/2n^2 + 1/3n^3 - \cdots$

Hence $1 = (n + a) (1/n - 1/2n^2 + 1/3n^3 - \cdots)$

$$= 1 + (-\tfrac{1}{2} + a)/n + (\tfrac{1}{3} - \tfrac{a}{2})/n^2 + \cdots$$

Hence if we write $a = +\dfrac{1}{2}$, the error in this expression is a term of order $1/12n^2$ compared with 1. Thus if n is so large that $1/12n^2$ can be neglected in comparison with 1, we may write approximately

$$e = \left(1 + \frac{1}{n}\right)^{n + \frac{1}{2}}$$

or $\left(1 + \dfrac{1}{n}\right)^n = e \left(1 + \dfrac{1}{n}\right)^{-\frac{1}{2}}$

or inverting both sides $\left(1 + \dfrac{1}{n}\right)^{-n} = e^{-1} \left(1 + \dfrac{1}{n}\right)^{\frac{1}{2}}$

Example : Approximate evaluation of e.

$$e = \left(1 + \frac{1}{n}\right)^n \left(1 + \frac{1}{n}\right)^{\frac{1}{2}}$$

Let $n = 5$

$$\left(1 + \frac{1}{n}\right)^n = 1 \cdot 2^5 = 2 \cdot 4883$$

$$\left(1 + \frac{1}{n}\right)^{\frac{1}{2}} = 1 \cdot 2^{\frac{1}{2}} = 1 \cdot 0954$$

Hence, approximately

$$e = 2 \cdot 4883 \times 1 \cdot 0954 = 2 \cdot 726$$

The error should be of the order $1/12n^2 = 1/300$ in comparison with 1. The actual value of e is $2 \cdot 718$, so that the error is $0 \cdot 008$ in $2 \cdot 718$, or 1 in 340, which is less than 1 in 300.

Exercise : Show that if n is as small as 2, this formula will give e correct to at least 2 per cent.

(III)

We have seen that

$$e = \left(1 + \frac{1}{n}\right)^n \left(1 + \frac{1}{n}\right)^{\frac{1}{2}}$$

represents a very good approximation. We can write this in the form

$$e = \frac{(n+1)^n}{n^n} \cdot \frac{\sqrt{(n+1)}}{\sqrt{n}}$$

or $n^n \cdot e = (n+1)^n \cdot \dfrac{\sqrt{(n+1)}}{\sqrt{n}}$

Let us write, in succession, $n = 2, 3, 4, \ldots n$, then it is approximately true that

$$2^2 \cdot e = 3^2 \sqrt{3} / \sqrt{2}$$
$$3^3 \cdot e = 4^3 \sqrt{4} / \sqrt{3}$$
$$4^4 \cdot e = 5^4 \sqrt{5} / \sqrt{4}$$
$$5^5 \cdot e = 6^5 \sqrt{6} / \sqrt{5}$$
$$\cdots \cdots \cdots \cdots$$
$$n^n \cdot e = (n+1)^n \sqrt{(n+1)} / \sqrt{n}$$

If we multiply all the terms on the left-hand side together and those on the right-hand side also, and cancel out the common factors, we are left with

$$2 \cdot n! \, e^{n-1} = (n+1)^n \sqrt{(n+1)} / \sqrt{2}$$

But $\quad e \cdot n^n \cdot \sqrt{n} = (n+1)^n \sqrt{(n+1)}$

so that $\quad 2 \cdot n! \, e_r^{n-1} = e n^n \sqrt{n} / \sqrt{2}$

or $\quad n! = (e^2/2\sqrt{2}) e^{-n} n^n \sqrt{n} = 2 \cdot 6 \, e^{-n} n^n \sqrt{n}$ approximately.

There is a mathematical theorem that says that an approximate expression for $n!$ is

$$\sqrt{(2\pi n)} e^{-n} n^n$$

This is known as *Stirling's Theorem*, and it will be noticed that this is what we have just proved, except that we have found the coefficient $2 \cdot 6$ in place of $\sqrt{(2\pi)}$, which is actually about $2 \cdot 566$.

The degree of accuracy of this approximation to $n!$ is not the same as that of each item used in proving it, but is equivalent to ignoring $1/12n$ in comparison with 1. Thus, if n be taken as 8, the value $\sqrt{(16\pi)} 8^8 e^{-8}$ should give 8! correct to nearly 1 per cent.

The student is advised to verify this by actual calculation.

(IV)

In this section we propose to use Stirling's approximation to $n!$ to obtain a modified form of Bernoulli's Theorem on probability, for a particular case that will be of importance to us later.

We will regard the probability of obtaining a head on tossing a coin as $1/2$. Suppose a coin is tossed $2n$ times. What is the probability that there will be a surplus $2r$ of heads over tails? This means that we are inquiring what is the probability of exactly $n+r$ heads and $n-r$ tails. We need not, of course, think of this in terms of tossing of coins only. Suppose a difficult target is being bombed and the probability of dropping a bomb in the target area is only $\frac{1}{2}$—that is to say, on the average only half the bombs fall within that area. We might inquire what is the probability that out of 100 bombs dropped in a series of raids, 70 will fall within the target area. In this case there will be a surplus of 40 successes over the number of failures, *i.e.* $n = 50$, $r = 20$, $n + r = 70$, $n - r = 30$. In cases such as these, Bernoulli's Theorem tells us that the required probability

$$P = \frac{(2n)!}{(n+r)!\,(n-r)!}\left(\frac{1}{2}\right)^{n+r}\left(\frac{1}{2}\right)^{n-r}$$

$$= \frac{(2n)!}{(n+r)!\,(n-r)!}\cdot\frac{1}{2^{2n}}$$

Now, using Stirling's Theorem,

$$(2n)! = (2n)^{2n}\,e^{-2n}\sqrt{(2\pi\cdot 2n)}$$

$$= 2^{2n}\,n^{2n+\frac{1}{2}}\,e^{-2n}\sqrt{(4\pi)}$$

Also $(n+r)! = (n+r)^{n+r}\,e^{-n-r}\sqrt{[2\pi(n+r)]}$

$$= n^{n+r+\frac{1}{2}}\left(1+\frac{r}{n}\right)^{n+r+\frac{1}{2}}e^{-n-r}\sqrt{(2\pi)}$$

and $(n-r)! = n^{n-r+\frac{1}{2}}\left(1-\frac{r}{n}\right)^{n-r+\frac{1}{2}}e^{-n+r}\sqrt{(2\pi)}$

so that $(n+r)!\,(n-r)!$

$$= n^{2n+1}\left(1-\frac{r^2}{n^2}\right)^{n+\frac{1}{2}}\left(1+\frac{r}{n}\right)^{r}\left(1-\frac{r}{n}\right)^{-r}e^{-2n}\cdot 2\pi$$

Therefore $\dfrac{(2n)!}{(n+r)!\,(n-r)!}\left(\dfrac{1}{2^{2n}}\right)$

$$= \frac{1}{\sqrt{(n\pi)}}\left(1-\frac{r^2}{n^2}\right)^{-n-\frac{1}{2}}\left(1+\frac{r}{n}\right)^{-r}\left(1-\frac{r}{n}\right)^{r}$$

$$= \frac{1}{\sqrt{(n\pi)}}\left(1-\frac{r^2}{n^2}\right)^{-\frac{n^2}{r^2}\cdot\frac{r^2}{n}}\left(1-\frac{r^2}{n^2}\right)^{-\frac{1}{2}}\left(1+\frac{r}{n}\right)^{\frac{n}{r}\left(-\frac{r^2}{n}\right)}\left(1-\frac{r}{n}\right)^{-\frac{n}{r}\left(-\frac{r^2}{n}\right)}$$

Now $\left(1-\dfrac{r^2}{n^2}\right)^{-\frac{n^2}{r^2}} \longrightarrow e$, as $\dfrac{n}{r}$ increases indefinitely

$$\left(1-\frac{r^2}{n^2}\right)^{\frac{1}{2}} \longrightarrow 1$$

$$\left(1+\frac{r}{n}\right)^{\frac{n}{r}} \longrightarrow e$$

$$\left(1-\frac{r}{n}\right)^{-\frac{n}{r}} \longrightarrow e$$

Therefore

$$\frac{(2n)!}{(n+r)!\,(n-r)!}\left(\frac{1}{2^{2n}}\right) \longrightarrow \frac{1}{\sqrt{(\pi n)}}\, e^{\frac{r^2}{n}}.e^{-\frac{r^2}{n}}.e^{-\frac{r^2}{n}}$$

$$\longrightarrow \frac{1}{\sqrt{(\pi n)}}\, e^{-\frac{r^2}{n}}$$

and this is the approximate expression for Bernoulli's value, if $\frac{r}{n}$ is small, in which case of course $\frac{n}{r}$ is large.

Example : To find the error in replacing $\dfrac{(2n)!}{(n+r)!\,(n-r)!}\dfrac{1}{2^{2n}}$ by $\dfrac{1}{\sqrt{(\pi n)}}\, e^{-r^2/n}$ for the case $n = 10, r = 2$.

$$\frac{20!}{12!\,8!\,2^{20}} = \frac{20 \times 19 \times 18 \times 17 \times 16 \times 15 \times 14 \times 13}{8 \times 7 \times 6 \times 5 \times 4 \times 3 \times 2 \times 2^{20}}$$

Cancelling out common factors and using four-figure logarithms, this gives a value of $0\cdot1203$.

Evaluating $\dfrac{1}{\sqrt{(\pi n)}}\, e^{-r^2/n}$, we find, again using four-figure logarithms,

$$\frac{1}{\sqrt{(10\pi)}}e^{-2/5} = 0\cdot1196$$

To the accuracy of these tables, with such a calculation, these two numbers are indistinguishable.

(v)

From the definition of e it is now clear that e^x is a function of x which is the limit of $\left(1+\dfrac{1}{n}\right)^{nx}$ when n increases indefinitely. By expanding in the same way as we did in the simple case of e, we easily find that

$$e^x = 1 + x + x^2/2! + x^3/3! + \cdot\cdot\cdot,$$

while e^{-x} is obtained by writing $-x$ for x in the above formula. It is clear that when $x = 1$ this is consistent with what we have already found for e.

(VI)

The function e^{-x^2} is therefore expressed as a sum of powers of x by inserting $-x^2$ for x in the above series of terms for e^x. Thus

$$e^{-x^2} = 1 - \frac{x^2}{1!} + \frac{x^4}{2!} - \frac{x^6}{3!} + \ldots$$

Hence also

$$e^{-h^2x^2} = 1 - \frac{h^2x^2}{1!} + \frac{h^4x^4}{2!} - \frac{h^6x^6}{3!} + \ldots$$

From this the differential coefficient of $e^{-h^2x^2}$ follows immediately; for, differentiating the right-hand side, term by term, we obtain

$$-\frac{2h^2x}{1!} + \frac{4h^4x^3}{2!} - \frac{6h^6x^5}{3!} + \ldots$$

$$= -2h^2x\left[1 - \frac{h^2x^2}{1!} + \frac{h^4x^4}{2!} - \ldots\right]$$

$$= -2h^2xe^{-h^2x^2}$$

The function e^x can be found in tables for a series of values of x, and from this we can easily tabulate the function e^{-x^2}.

Here are some of the values, and in Fig. 20 they have been plotted so that we may see how this function varies in amount.

x	0	0·5	1·0	1·5	2	2·5	3
e^{-x^2}	1	0·7788	0·3679	0·1054	0·0183	0·0019	0·0001

We notice that the function does not change in form or in value by writing $-x$ in place of x, since x enters as x^2. Thus the curve is symmetrical about the axis of y. Also as x increases

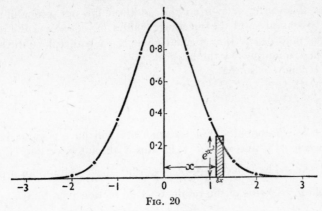

Fig. 20

in amount, e^{-x^2} diminishes in value, approaching zero as x increases indefinitely. Thus the curve falls off on both sides towards the axis of x, but never actually reaches it. Notice that it has the characteristic appearance of some of the distribution curves we have plotted. We shall see shortly that this is to be expected.

(VII)

It can be shown that the total area between this curve and the axis of x, extending from the extreme left to the extreme right, is $\sqrt{\pi}$. Stated otherwise, this says that the integral from $+\infty$ to $-\infty$ of $\dfrac{1}{\sqrt{\pi}} e^{-x^2}$ is 1,

$$i.e. \int_{-\infty}^{+\infty} \frac{1}{\sqrt{\pi}} e^{-x^2} dx = 1$$

(VIII)

If $f(x)\delta x$ is the probability that a quantity x has a value lying between x and $x + \delta x$, then the probability that the quantity will lie between any two numbers A and B is $\int_{A}^{B} f(x)dx$.

This follows at once from the addition law for probabilities. For we simply add the successive values of $f(x)\delta x$ over the total range A to B, and if δx is small enough, we can replace the sum of these quantities by the integral.

It follows also that

$$\int\limits_{-\infty}^{+\infty} f(x)dx = 1$$

since the probability that the quantity will have a value lying between $+\infty$ and $-\infty$ is 1, for this is absolutely certain.

Note.—The function $\dfrac{1}{\sqrt{\pi}}\,e^{-x^2}$ satisfies this condition for a probability, in virtue of the result stated in section VII.

EXERCISES

1. Evaluate $\left(1 + \dfrac{1}{n}\right)^n$ for $n = 1, 2, 3, 4, 10, 20, 30, 40, 50, 100$. Draw a graph of these values and estimate the limit to which $\left(1 + \dfrac{1}{n}\right)^n$ tends as n increases.

2. From the series for e, calculate the value of e correct to three decimal places, and compare your result with the answer to the last question.

3. Expand $\left(1 + \dfrac{x}{n}\right)^n$ by the Binomial Theorem. Hence deduce that $\left(1 + \dfrac{x}{n}\right)^n$ approaches $1 + \dfrac{x}{1!} + \dfrac{x^2}{2!} + \dfrac{x^3}{3!} + \ldots$ as n is indefinitely increased.

4. Find α and β so that if we write

$$e = \left(1 + \dfrac{1}{n}\right)^{n + \alpha + \frac{\beta}{n}}$$

this may be correct as far as terms in $\dfrac{1}{n^2}$ in the expansion on the right.

5. A coin is tossed 20 times. Estimate the probability of obtaining exactly 10 heads by using Stirling's approximation to $n!$

6. Plot on the same diagram the graphs of $n!$ and $\sqrt{2\pi n}\, e^{-n} n^n$ against n from $n = 1$ to $n = 10$.

Draw the variation in the percentage error in the latter regarded as an approximate to $n!$.

7. Differentiate the following expressions with respect to x :

(1) e^{-x} ; (2) $5e^{4x}$; (3) $(n + 1)e^x$; (4) e^{-x^2} ; (5) $e^{-n^2 x^2}$

(6) xe^x ; (7) $xe^{-h^2 x^2}$

CHAPTER XII

GAUSS'S LAW OF ERROR—I

DISTRIBUTION OF ERRORS ABOUT THE MEAN

A SERIES of measurements are made of the same thing. They differ among themselves. Why?

We adopt as a theory of how these differences arise, that in any measurement a very large number of small variations intrude themselves, each separately indistinguishable ; that together they sum up to give an error in each case different from that found on the next occasion. These small variations may be thought of as arising from external conditions over which one may be unable to exercise control, such as changes in temperature and in pressure of the atmosphere, whereby the actual instruments are themselves affected slightly. Heat may be radiated from the body of the experimenter with similar effects. In the setting of an instrument there may be slight tremors of the hand, or the instruments may be shaken slightly out of their setting during the course of the experiment by earth tremors due to the passage of traffic. A thousand and one small factors of this nature may enter into any particular measurement giving a sum total error—the error of the observation. It is not in general possible to track down these detailed effects. If it were they could be systematically eliminated, and those that can be so tracked down are naturally assumed in any good experiment to have been so removed. When all *systematic* errors of this nature have been ousted, there still remains a multitude of very small effects. It is the sum of these, some of which are positive in their influence, some negative, with which we are concerned. Further, let each of these small contributory errors be of equal amount E, positive or negative, and in any particular case let us suppose there are $2n$ of them. The total error produced will range from $2n$E to $-2n$E, the two extreme cases where they are all positive and all negative respectively. Suppose in our case there is a surplus of positive errors equal in number to $2r$, giving therefore a total positive error of $2r$E. If x is the size of the total error, then

$$x = 2r\mathrm{E}$$

For this to occur with a total of $2n$ errors there must be $n + r$ positive errors and $n - r$ negative errors.

Let us first examine the probability with which an error of this magnitude $2r$E will occur. In effect this asks for the probability that in $2n$ trials there shall be $n + r$ successes (positive errors) and $n - r$ failures (negative errors). For our purpose, of course, it is immaterial which we call successes and which failures. Since we assume that all these tiny errors are of equal magnitude, and that a positive error is just as likely to occur as a negative one, we take as the probability of a tiny positive error a value of $1/2$. Hence, applying Bernouilli's Theorem, we find that the probability that a total positive error of amount $2r$E may arise is

$$\frac{(2n)!}{(n + r)! \, (n - r)! \, 2^{n+r} \, 2^{n-r}}$$

In this n is presumed to be large. Accordingly we can approximate to this expression by Stirling's Theorem. In fact, this has already been done in the previous chapter, section IV, enabling us to conclude that out of $2n$ total errors each of magnitude E, the probability that they will combine to form a total positive error of $2r$E is

$$\frac{1}{\sqrt{(\pi n)}} e^{-r^2/n} .$$

As long as we think of the total error x as composed of separate and discrete known errors E, this result has a meaning, but in fact, of course, we have no information regarding the elementary errors E. It is the composite error x with which we have to deal. For example, if we know that the distribution curve or frequency curve for deviations from the mean of the observations lies symmetrically about that mean, we might take the latter as the best value, and the deviations of readings from it then rank as the total errors. Proceeding a stage further, in practice if we think of a distribution curve as ultimately in the nature of a histogram, as it undoubtedly is, we do not talk of an error of exactly x, but of one lying within a certain range, say x to $x + \delta x$. All those readings that give deviations lying in this interval are in practice grouped together, and loosely referred to as at x. If therefore we wish to switch attention from the unknown elementary errors E to the errors x, because they are more capable of direct examination, we have to reinterpret our result in terms of x and $x + \delta x$. What we are really seeking, therefore, is the probability with which a total error lying between x and $x + \delta x$ may be committed. All we know about n is that it is large, and all we know of x is that it is proportional to r. The form of the approximation we have found for the probability, especially the term $e^{-r^2/n}$, suggests that since x is proportional to r, and n is after all simply a large constant, we should write, instead of $x = 2r\text{E}$, rather $hx = r/\sqrt{n}$ where h is some constant. Thus the term $e^{-r^2/n}$ would be written $e^{-h^2 x^2}$. This is done, of course, only for mathematical convenience, but it does not violate our assumption that the total error is proportional to r. In this expression for x, the number r is a whole number. Any change in x occurs because of a change in r, and the smallest possible change in r is 1.

Thus $$h\delta x = 1/\sqrt{n},$$

for $h\delta x$ is the corresponding small change in hx.

Now this expression comes into the formula for the probability as part of the coefficient of the exponential term. Thus, if we replace r^2/n by $h^2 x^2$ and $1/\sqrt{n}$ by $h\delta x$ in $\dfrac{1}{\sqrt{(\pi n)}} e^{-r^2/n}$, the expression for the probability takes a form more suited to our needs. It says that the probability of an error of magnitude x occurring, or (more accurately in practice) the probability of an error occurring in the range x to $x + \delta x$ is $\dfrac{h}{\sqrt{\pi}} e^{-h^2 x^2} \delta x$. This, known as Gauss's Law, is an important expression because it provides us with an idealized error distribution, built up on the assumption that the elementary errors that constitute the total have occurred at random or by pure chance. In that sense it provides

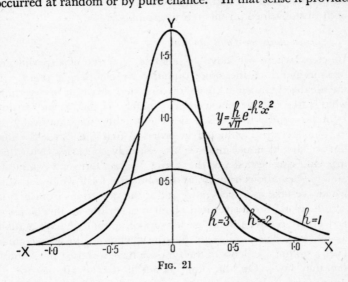

$$y = \frac{h}{\sqrt{\pi}} e^{-h^2 x^2}$$

Fig. 21

us with a *standard error law*, against which we can see the significance of an actual distribution of this nature as it occurs in practice. In Fig. 21 the curves of

$$y = \frac{h}{\sqrt{\pi}} e^{-h^2 x^2}$$

are drawn on a horizontal base x for various values of h. They lie, as we expect, symmetrically about the y-axis, running ultimately into the x-axis at a great distance from the origin. The former property indicates that the probability of committing an error lying in any range to one side of the y-axis is the same as the probability of committing an error lying in the same range but on the other side. The latter property shows that the probability of committing a very large error positive or negative falls off progressively to zero as the presumed error increases.

The reader is advised at this stage to return to the chapter on frequency curves and compare the shape of those given there with this obtained on theoretical grounds.

Comparison with the Gaussian Curve

In cases where we have to analyse a series of experimental measurements of the same quantity by comparing them with the idealized Gaussian curve, the first step clearly is to determine what value can be taken approximately as the " true " value. It might appear that this is also the last step since naturally the experiments are conducted in order to find the " true " value, but we should notice that we are not only concerned with finding what can be taken as the " true " value, but with examining how the deviations from it are distributed ; for if we find a value which we take as a true value and if the deviations from it (that is, the errors) are distributed about it according to this Gaussian Law, there is obviously a case for supposing that we have actually found the " true " value in that the deviation can be accounted for by simple accidents of the type we have assumed in establishing that law. On the other hand, if the deviations are not distributed in this way, we have either not found a good estimate of the true value, or some systematic effect is showing itself in our measurements and entering as a so-called error. We shall begin by assuming that the average of the readings is not far removed from the " true " value. What we have called x in the Gaussian formula then becomes the difference of the observations from this average, and these sets of differences can be grouped to lie within regular ranges just as we have grouped the data in Chapter II. when drawing a distribution curve. In fact, the first step in the analysis of a set of observations is to set up a distribution table and a histogram of deviations from the

average. Horizontally we would have x as the distance from
the origin to the centre of each interval, and δx would be the
actual width of this interval. The Gaussian formula will then
enable a comparison to be made, where the interval within
which the observations are grouped is δx, a definite small constant.
Vertically, instead of each ordinate being the total number of
readings that have deviations that fall in the interval from x to
$x + \delta x$ we could make the ordinate 1/N of this, where N is the
total number of observations. We would then have a probability histogram, and it is this that we would require to compare
with the appropriate standard Gaussian curves in Fig. 21.

Finding the Appropriate Gaussian Curve

How are we to find which Gaussian curve is the proper one
for comparison ? What in fact is the proper value for h for any
given set of data ? For this purpose let us examine the Gaussian
curve a little more closely. $\dfrac{h}{\sqrt{\pi}} e^{-h^2 x^2} \delta x$ is the probability that
the deviation lies between x and $x + \delta x$. The probability that
it lies in a wider range, say between a and b, will be the sum
of these probabilities for each of the shorter intervals δx in the
range a to b, or, as we could put it in this case, the integral of
this expression from a to b. As it is absolutely certain that an
error must lie between $+ \infty$ and $- \infty$, it follows that

$$\int_{-\infty}^{\infty} \frac{h}{\sqrt{\pi}} e^{-h^2 x^2} dx = 1$$

or

$$\int_{-\infty}^{\infty} e^{-h^2 x^2} dx = \sqrt{\pi}/h$$

Note.—Compare this result for $h = 1$ with that stated in
Chapter XI, section VII.

The expressions on the left and on the right are functions
of h only. We propose to differentiate both sides with respect

to h, a step which can be justified mathematically, but we do not propose to do so here ; thus

$$\int_{-\infty}^{\infty} - 2hx^2 e^{-h^2x^2} dx = -\sqrt{\pi}/h^2$$

or

$$\frac{h}{\sqrt{\pi}}\int_{-\infty}^{\infty} x^2 e^{-h^2x^2} dx = \frac{1}{2h^2}$$

Now consider σ the standard deviation for a set of observations that exactly fit the Gaussian curve. If we take the sum of the squares of the errors divided by the total number of errors we shall obtain σ^2. If N is the total number of observations, then since $\frac{h}{\sqrt{\pi}} e^{-h^2x^2} \delta x$ is the proportion that falls in the range x to $x + \delta x$, then $\frac{Nh}{\sqrt{\pi}}e^{-h^2x^2} \delta x$ will be the actual number that fall in this range. We have to multiply this by x^2, and sum this up over the whole range $+\infty$ to $+\infty$. This will give the sum of the squares of the deviations from the mean. We then divide by N. Thus

$$\sigma^2 = \frac{1}{N} \int_{-\infty}^{\infty} \frac{Nhx^2}{\sqrt{\pi}} e^{-h^2x^2} dx$$

$$= \frac{h}{\sqrt{\pi}} \int_{-\infty}^{\infty} x^2 e^{-h^2x^2} dx$$

$$= 1/2h^2, \text{ as already found.}$$

Accordingly $h = 1/\sigma\sqrt{2}$.

Our Gaussian formula becomes, therefore, $\dfrac{1}{\sigma\sqrt{(2\pi)}} e^{-\frac{x^2}{2\sigma^2}} \delta x$ on replacing h by $1/\sigma\sqrt{2}$, where σ is the standard deviation of the set of observations that fit the Gaussian curve.

A comparison, therefore, between our actual observations and the Gaussian curve may be made by identifying the value of σ with that obtained directly from the observations. Plotting the now definite Gaussian curve, we can compare it with the probability histogram found directly from the data.

Example.—Let us illustrate this by determining the Gaussian curve corresponding to the histogram showing the frequency of

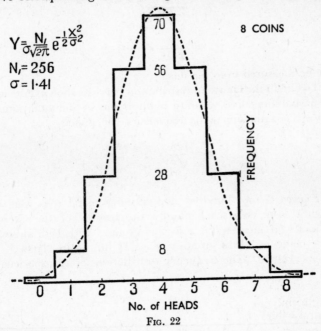

$$Y = \frac{N_i}{\sigma\sqrt{2\pi}}\, e^{-\frac{1}{2}\frac{X^2}{\sigma^2}}$$

$N_i = 256$

$\sigma = 1.41$

8 COINS

FREQUENCY

No. of HEADS

Fig. 22

occurrence of heads when eight coins are tossed. The frequencies are of course the binomial coefficients discussed in Chapter V, and they are set out in No. 3 of the exercises as follows :

Number of Heads	0	1	2	3	4	5	6	7	8
Frequency	1	8	28	56	70	56	28	8	1

The histogram is shown in Fig. 22, where the number of heads is placed at the centre of each range. The mean is of course 4, since in this case $N = 8$, and the standard deviation $\sigma = \frac{1}{2} \sqrt{N} = \frac{1}{2} \sqrt{8} = \sqrt{2}$. These could have been calculated directly instead of from the formulæ of Chapter V. In this case the interval δx is 1. The Gaussian probability curve is therefore

$$y = \frac{1}{\sigma \sqrt{(2\pi)}} e^{-x^2/2\sigma^2}$$

$$= \frac{1}{2\sqrt{\pi}} e^{-x^2/4}$$

x being measured from the mean.

To obtain the Gaussian distribution curve as shown, instead of the probability curve, we must multiply this by the total number of events, viz. the sum of the frequencies, 256, giving

$$y = \frac{128}{\sqrt{\pi}} e^{-x^2/4}$$

Example.—Two hundred and fifty-five metal rods were cut roughly 6 in. oversize. Finally the lengths of the oversize amount were measured exactly and grouped with 1-in. intervals, there being in all 12 groups : $\frac{1}{2}$ in.–$1\frac{1}{2}$ in., $1\frac{1}{2}$ in.–$2\frac{1}{2}$ in., . . . $11\frac{1}{2}$ in.–$12\frac{1}{2}$ in. The frequency distribution for the 255 lengths was :

Length (in.) Central values	1	2	3	4	5	6	7	8	9	10	11	12
Frequency	2	10	19	25	40	44	41	28	25	15	5	1

It is required to fit a Gaussian curve to this distribution.

From the theory we have already considered the number of observations falling within a range x to $x + \delta x$ *measured from the mean* is

$$\frac{N}{\sigma \sqrt{(2\pi)}} e^{-\frac{x}{2\sigma^2}} \delta x$$

where N is the total number of observations, and σ the standard deviation. In this case $N = 255$.

Thus, we first require to find the mean and the standard deviation of the given observations. The work is best set out in columns, and using the short method as explained in Chapter IV we take an assumed average (A) of 6 inches.

Length (inches)	Frequency (f)	x	fx	x^2	fx^2
1	2	-5	-10	25	50
2	10	-4	-40	16	160
3	19	-3	-57	9	171
4	25	-2	-50	4	100
5	40	-1	-40	1	40
6	44	0		0	0
7	41	1	$+41$	1	41
8	28	2	$+56$	4	112
9	25	3	$+75$	9	225
10	15	4	$+60$	16	240
11	5	5	$+25$	25	125
12	1	6	$+6$	36	36
	255		$-197 + 263$ $= +66$		1300

The third column gives the deviations from the assumed mean and the fourth column gives the product of these deviations and the frequency with which they occur. The sum of this column is $+66$, which is the total amount, spread over 255 observations, by which the assumed mean is " out."

If M represents the true mean, then

$$M = A + \frac{66}{255}$$

$$= 6 \cdot 259 \text{ in.}$$

From Chapter IV if σ is the true standard deviation and s the standard deviation about the assumed mean

$$\sigma^2 = s^2 - (M - A)^2$$

In this example column six gives the fictitious standard deviation s, because $s^2 = \dfrac{1300}{255} = 5\cdot098$.

Therefore $\sigma^2 = 5\cdot098 - (0\cdot259)^2$
                    $= 5\cdot031$
Thus $\sigma = 2\cdot243$ in.

We are now in a position to draw the Gaussian curve

$$y = \frac{N}{\sigma\sqrt{(2\pi)}}\ e^{-\frac{x^2}{2\sigma^2}}$$

$$= \frac{255}{2\cdot243\sqrt{(2\pi)}}\ e^{-\frac{x^2}{10\cdot062}} = 45\cdot35\ e^{-0\cdot0994x^2}$$

Taking logarithms

$$\log y = \log 45\cdot35 - 0\cdot0994x^2 \log e$$
$$= 1\cdot65663 - 0\cdot04316x^2$$

From this relation we can draw up a table giving the values of $\log y$, and consequently y for different values of x, from which we can draw the Gaussian curve.

x	0	± 1	± 2	± 3	± 4	± 5	± 6
$\log y$	1·65663	1·61347	1·48400	1·26819	0·96605	0·5776	0·10283
y	45·35	41·06	30·48	18·54	9·25	3·78	1·27

To plot the curve the histogram is first drawn, the position of the mean (6·259 inches) being indicated by the vertical line. The table above then gives the theoretical frequency for values of x ; 1, 2, 3, 4, 5, or 6 inches on either side of the mean, and measured from this mean (see Fig. 23).

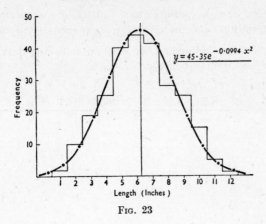

$$y = 45 \cdot 35e^{-0 \cdot 0994\ x^2}$$

Length (Inches)

Fig. 23

EXERCISES

1. From the following frequency table of heights find the equation to the frequency curve—

h = height in inches   f = frequency

h	55	57	59	61	63	65	67	69
f	6	49	228	597	692	386	114	24

2. Fit a Gaussian curve to the following frequency distribution; also draw the histogram and plot the curve:

Observation Central Values (inches)	59·5	62·5	65·5	68·5	71·5	74·5	77·5	80·5
Frequency	4	24	188	404	387	158	30	5

3. Draw the Gaussian probability curve having the same standard deviation as that of the following data:

Measurement	8–9	9–10	10–11	11–12	12–13	13–14
Frequency	1	5	10	10	5	1

Estimate the probability that a random measurement will have a deviation from the mean lying between − 0·5 and 1·8.

4. Fit a Gaussian frequency curve to the following data. Draw the curve and the frequency polygon.

Length of line in cm.	8·60	8·59	8·58	8·57	8·56	8·55	8·54	8·53	8·52
Frequency	2	3	4	9	10	8	4	1	1

CHAPTER XIII

GAUSS'S LAW OF ERROR—II

SOME PROPERTIES OF THE LAW

THIS law states that in the idealized form the probability of an error having a magnitude that lies between x and $x + \delta x$ is

$$\frac{1}{\sigma\sqrt{(2\pi)}} \, e^{-x^2/2\sigma^2} \, \delta x$$

In this σ is the standard deviation of the system of idealized readings. Let us examine the nature of the curve

$$y = \frac{1}{\sigma\sqrt{(2\pi)}} \, e^{-x^2/2\sigma^2}$$

We have already seen that this reaches its greatest value when $x = 0$ at which point the ordinate is $1/\sigma\sqrt{(2\pi)}$. The curve then falls off on both sides towards the x axis, gradually falling closer and closer to it, but never actually reaching it. Where the graph crosses the axis of y it curves downwards. Farther to the right and left the curve bends in the opposite direction. At some intermediate position, therefore, the curvature changes sign. The point at which this occurs is called a " point of inflection." It represents the position where the slope of the tangent having increased numerically from $x = 0$ begins to decrease again ; that is, it is a position of maximum slope. Mathematically, therefore, this means that the differential coefficient which measures the slope at that position is a maximum.

The mathematical condition, therefore, is that the differential coefficient of this differential coefficient must be zero. Accordingly, to find where this occurs we have to differentiate $\frac{1}{\sigma\sqrt{(2\pi)}} \, e^{-x^2/2\sigma^2}$ twice, and equate the result to zero. The first differential coefficient is (Chapter XI, section VI)

$$- \frac{x}{\sigma^3 \sqrt{(2\pi)}} \, e^{-x^2/2\sigma^2}$$

Since we are to equate the differential coefficient of this to zero we will ignore the constant. Thus differentiating $xe^{-x^2/2\sigma^2}$ and equating to zero we find

$$e^{-x^2/2\sigma^2} - \frac{x^2}{\sigma^2} \, e^{-x^2/2\sigma^2} = 0$$

or $\quad \left(1 - \frac{x^2}{\sigma^2}\right) e^{-x^2/2\sigma^2} = 0$

Since the exponential term is always positive this demands that $x = \pm \sigma$. *Thus the point of inflection occurs at a distance from the origin, equal to the standard deviation.*

Practical Steps in Drawing the Probability Curve

For the purpose of drawing the probability curve, therefore, this fact may be of use. We first calculate the standard deviation σ, draw the two vertical lines at $x = \sigma$ and $x = -\sigma$, and we know that as the curve crosses this line it changes from a downward curvature to an upward curvature.

Certain points are easily fixed on the curve. When $x = 0$ the value of y is $\dfrac{1}{\sigma \sqrt{(2\pi)}}$, which of course is easily calculated once σ is known. Call this A ; at the point of inflection where $x = \sigma$ the value of y is $\dfrac{1}{\sigma \sqrt{(2\pi)}} \, e^{-\sigma^2/2\sigma^2} = \dfrac{1}{\sigma \sqrt{(2\pi)}} \cdot \dfrac{1}{\sqrt{e}}$. Thus the ordinate, say B, at $x = \sigma$ and of course also at $x = -\sigma$ is $A/\sqrt{e}$, that is, $0 \cdot 61A$. This fixes the position of the point of inflection.

The slope of the graph at any point x is $- \dfrac{x}{\sigma^3 \sqrt{(2\pi)}} e^{-x^2/2\sigma^2}$

Thus at the point of inflection where $x = \sigma$ this slope is

$$- \frac{1}{\sigma^2 \sqrt{(2\pi)}} \cdot \frac{1}{\sqrt{e}} = - \frac{A/\sqrt{e}}{\sigma} = - \frac{B}{\sigma}$$

This gives a simple graphical method of drawing the slope at this point, as can be seen from the annexed diagram. P is the point distant σ, the standard deviation, from 0. The ordinate

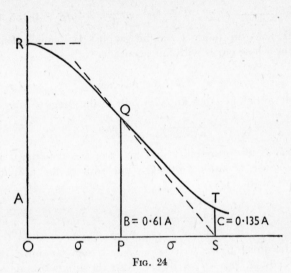

FIG. 24

OR = A is where the curve crosses the axis of y. The ordinate to the point of inflection is PQ = B. The slope of the tangent at Q is B/σ. Thus the tangent at Q is SQ, where PS = σ.

Thus the curve turns downwards at R, approaches the tangent at Q from underneath, and *crosses* the tangent to the upper side beyond Q, as shown by the curve RQ.

With this information the curve can quickly be drawn with fair accuracy. The steps are as follows :

(i) Calculate σ the standard deviation from the data supplied.

(ii) Fix the point R by calculating $A = 1/\sigma\sqrt{(2\pi)}$.

(iii) Fix the points P and S at distances σ and 2σ from O.

(iv) Fix the point Q by calculating $B = A/\sqrt{e}$.

(v) Join SQ, which is the tangent to the curve at Q.

(vi) It remains only to fix one other point (T) beyond P, say at S, where $PS = \sigma$.

Here $x = 2\sigma$. Thus the ordinate is

$$C = \frac{1}{\sigma\sqrt{(2\pi)}} e^{-4\sigma^2/2\sigma^2} = 1/e^2\sigma\sqrt{(2\pi)} = A/e^2 = 0.135 \ A.$$

This fixes the point T on the graph. It is now possible to draw the whole curve with fair accuracy.

The Error Function

The probability that an error falls in the range x to $x + \delta x$ is

$$\frac{1}{\sigma\sqrt{(2\pi)}} e^{-x^2/2\sigma^2}\delta x.$$

What is the probability that an error lies between 0 and σ, the standard deviation? Clearly the sum of the probabilities over this range, viz. :

$$\int_0^\sigma \frac{1}{\sigma\sqrt{(2\pi)}} e^{-x^2/2\sigma^2}dx.$$

If in this integral we write $t = x/\sigma\sqrt{2}$ then we must replace $dx/\sigma\sqrt{2}$ by dt, and $x^2/2\sigma^2$ by t^2. Also the limits 0 and σ for x must be replaced by the corresponding limits 0 and $1/\sqrt{2}$ for t obtained by inserting these values of x in $t = x/\sigma\sqrt{2}$. Thus the probability that an error falls in the range 0 to σ is :

$$\int_0^\sigma \frac{1}{\sigma\sqrt{(2\pi)}} e^{-x^2/2\sigma} \ dx = \frac{1}{\sqrt{\pi}} \int_0^{\frac{1}{\sqrt{2}}} e^{-t^2} \ dt$$

It follows that the probability that an error falls in the range $-\sigma$ to $+\sigma$ is

$$\frac{2}{\sqrt{\pi}} \int_0^{\frac{1}{\sqrt{2}}} e^{-t^2} \ dt$$

In the same way, if we wish to have the probability that an error will fall in the range $+2\sigma$ to -2σ, we would clearly have to evaluate the same integral except that the range would be different, viz.:

$$\frac{2}{\sqrt{\pi}} \int_0^{\frac{2}{\sqrt{2}}} e^{-t^2} dt$$

For a range $+3\sigma$ to -3σ the value of the corresponding probability would be $\dfrac{2}{\sqrt{\pi}} \displaystyle\int_0^{\frac{3}{\sqrt{2}}} e^{-t^2} dt$, and generally for a range $a\sigma$ to $-a\sigma$, where a is any number, the probability would be

$$\frac{2}{\sqrt{\pi}} \int_0^{\frac{a}{\sqrt{2}}} e^{-t^2} dt$$

Each of these integrals is, of course, a definite number. Its importance lies in the fact that being a probability it gives us the proportion of idealised observations that should fall in the range specified. We shall see in a moment how this works itself out in practice.

Our first task, therefore, is to determine the numbers that correspond to each of these integrals. Interpreting them as areas they clearly respond to $2/\sqrt{\pi}$ times the area between the curve $y = e^{-x^2}$, and the x axis between $x = 0$, and $x = 1/\sqrt{2}$, $2/\sqrt{2}$, $3/\sqrt{2}$, . . . $a/\sqrt{2}$ respectively.

This means that $\dfrac{2}{\sqrt{\pi}} \displaystyle\int_0^x e^{-t^2} dt$, which is dependent only on x

is an important function of x for our purpose. It is called the *Error Function*, and is usually written Erf x for short.

Now we already know (Chapter XI, section VII) that

$$\int_0^{\infty} e^{-t^2} dt = \sqrt{\pi}/2$$

so that
$$\frac{2}{\sqrt{\pi}}\int_0^\infty e^{-t^2}dt = 1$$

and the value of
$$\mathrm{Erf}\, x = \frac{2}{\sqrt{\pi}}\int_0^x e^{-t^2}dt$$

for any other value of x will, therefore, be less than 1, remembering that e^{-t^2} is itself a function that is always positive and diminishes to zero as t increases indefinitely.

It is not our purpose here to examine the nature of $\mathrm{Erf}\, x$. We merely state that there is no simple form of a compact nature in terms of which it can be expressed, but its value has been calculated for successive values of x, and these are provided in the accompanying table on page 155.

For example, we see that when $x = 0\cdot30$ the value of $\mathrm{Erf}\,(0\cdot30)$ is $0\cdot32863$, and when $x = 1\cdot00$, $\mathrm{Erf}\,(1\cdot00)$ is $0\cdot84270$.

From this table we can read off the probabilities that errors will fall between $+\,\sigma$ and $-\,\sigma$ for in that case we require the value of $\mathrm{Erf}\,(1/\sqrt{2}) = \mathrm{Erf}\,0\cdot707$.

Now from the table $\mathrm{Erf}\,0\cdot70 = 0\cdot67780$
and $\mathrm{Erf}\,0\cdot72 = 0\cdot69143$.

Since $0\cdot707$ is seven-twentieths towards $0\cdot72$ from $0\cdot70$ approximately, we add to $0\cdot67780$, seven-twentieths of $0\cdot69143 - 0\cdot67780$, i.e., we add $0\cdot00477$.

Thus $\mathrm{Erf}\,(1/\sqrt{2}) = 0\cdot67780 + 0\cdot00477 = 0\cdot68257$
$= 0\cdot683$ approximately.

This means that out of 1,000 observations with errors that follow the Gaussian Law, 683 would have errors lying in the range $+\,\sigma$ to $-\,\sigma$. Stated otherwise, this asserts that 317 out of 1,000 would have errors outside this range.

In the same way we find from the tables that when the range is $+\,2\sigma$ to $-\,2\sigma$

$\mathrm{Erf}\,(2/\sqrt{2}) \quad = \mathrm{Erf}\,1\cdot414$
$\mathrm{Erf}\,1\cdot40 \quad = 0\cdot95229$

$$\text{Erf } 1\cdot 42 \qquad = 0\cdot 95538$$
$$\text{Difference} \quad = 0\cdot 00309$$

Since 1·414 is seven-tenths on the way to 1·42 from 1·40 we have to add this fraction of 0·00309 to 0·95229.

Thus finally

$$\text{Erf}(2/\sqrt{2}) = \text{Erf } 1\cdot 414 = 0\cdot 95445$$
$$= 0\cdot 954 \text{ approximately}$$

Accordingly, out of 1,000 observations 954 would fall in the range $+ 2\sigma$ to $- 2\sigma$, or, stated otherwise, 46 out of 1,000 would fall outside this range.

In this way, therefore, we can calculate the numbers out of every thousand that should fall, in the idealized case, *outside* any specified range, and the results so found can be shown graphically as in the annexed diagram.

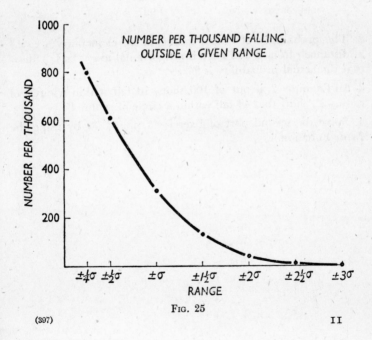

FIG. 25

EXERCISES

1. Verify that the probabilities of a set of idealized observations having errors that fall within the range specified in column 1 of the following table are given in column 2 of that table, and the number per thousand outside the specified range in column 3.

Range	Probability	Number per 1,000 outside the specified Range
$+ \frac{1}{4}\sigma$ to $- \frac{1}{4}\sigma$	0·198	802
$+ \frac{1}{2}\sigma$ to $- \frac{1}{2}\sigma$	0·383	617
$+ \sigma$ to $- \sigma$	0·683	317
$+ \frac{3}{2}\sigma$ to $- \frac{3}{2}\sigma$	0·866	134
$+ 2\sigma$ to $- 2\sigma$	0·954	46
$+ 3\sigma$ to $- 3\sigma$	0·997	3

2. The probability of a shot falling in an elementary area dA at distance r from a bull's eye is proportional to $e^{-h^2r^2}dA$. Show that the actual probability is $2h^2re^{-h^2r^2}dr$.

3. In Example 2, if out of 100 shots, 10 fall within a circle of radius 2″, show that 44 fall within a circle of radius 4″.

4. Solve the second part of Exercise 3, pp. 145-6, by using the Error Function.

$$\text{Erf } x = \frac{2}{\sqrt{\pi}} \int_0^x e^{-t^2} \, dt.$$

x	Erf x	x	Erf x	x	Erf x
0·02	0·02256	1·02	0·85084	2·02	0·99572
0·04	0·04511	1·04	0·85865	2·04	0·99609
0·06	0·06762	1·06	0·86614	2·06	0·99642
0·08	0·09008	1·08	0·87333	2·08	0·99673
0·10	0·11246	1·10	0·88021	2·10	0·99702
0·12	0·13476	1·12	0·88679	2·12	0·99728
0·14	0·15695	1·14	0·89308	2·14	0·99753
0·16	0·17901	1·16	0·89910	2·16	0·99775
0·18	0·20093	1·18	0·90484	2·18	0·99795
0·20	0·22270	1·20	0·91031	2·20	0·99814
0·22	0·24430	1·22	0·91553	2·22	0·99831
0·24	0·26570	1·24	0·92051	2·24	0·99846
0·26	0·28690	1·26	0·92524	2·26	0·99861
0·28	0·30788	1·28	0·92973	2·28	0·99874
0·30	0·32863	1·30	0·93401	2·30	0·99886
0·32	0·34913	1·32	0·93807	2·32	0·99897
0·34	0·36936	1·34	0·94191	2·34	0·99906
0·36	0·38933	1·36	0·94556	2·36	0·99915
0·38	0·40901	1·38	0·94902	2·38	0·99924
0·40	0·42839	1·40	0·95229	2·40	0·99931
0·42	0·44747	1·42	0·95538	2·42	0·99938
0·44	0·46623	1·44	0·95830	2·44	0·99944
0·46	0·48466	1·46	0·96105	2·46	0·99950
0·48	0·50275	1·48	0·96365	2·48	0·99955
0·50	0·52050	1·50	0·96611	2·50	0·99959
0·52	0·53790	1·52	0·96841	2·52	0·99963
0·54	0·55494	1·54	0·97059	2·54	0·99967
0·56	0·57162	1·56	0·97263	2·56	0·99971
0·58	0·58792	1·58	0·97455	2·58	0·99974
0·60	0·60386	1·60	0·97635	2·60	0·99976
0·62	0·61941	1·62	0·97804	2·62	0·99979
0·64	0·63459	1·64	0·97962	2·64	0·99981
0·66	0·64938	1·66	0·98110	2·66	0·99983
0·68	0·66378	1·68	0·98249	2·68	0·99985
0·70	0·67780	1·70	0·98379	2·70	0·99987
0·72	0·69143	1·72	0·98500	2·72	0·99988
0·74	0·70468	1·74	0·98613	2·74	0·99989
0·76	0·71754	1·76	0·98719	2·76	0·99991
0·78	0·73001	1·78	0·98817	2·78	0·99992
0·80	0·74210	1·80	0·98909	2·80	0·99992
0·82	0·75381	1·82	0·98994	2·82	0·99993
0·84	0·76514	1·84	0·99074	2·84	0·99994
0·86	0·77610	1·86	0·99147	2·86	0·99995
0·88	0·78669	1·88	0·99216	2·88	0·99995
0·90	0·79691	1·90	0·99279	2·90	0·99996
0·92	0·80677	1·92	0·99338	2·92	0·99996
0·94	0·81627	1·94	0·99392	2·94	0·99997
0·96	0·82542	1·96	0·99443	2·96	0·99997
0·98	0·83423	1·98	0·99489	2·98	0·99997
1·00	0·84270	2·00	0·99532	3·00	0·99998

CHAPTER XIV

ELEMENTS OF QUALITY CONTROL

In this chapter we turn to a question which is of first-class importance in any problem of production : by this we mean not only the production of large quantities of materials of given specification, but the production of trained men and women qualified to carry through certain operations with a given degree of precision. To produce a good marksman or an accurate bomb-aimer is, in principle, not different from turning out accurate machine parts in a factory ; the difference lies in the fact that in the first case the individual marksman has to learn or be trained to be accurate, whereas in the second case the machine part has to be turned out with a certain degree of precision. In the latter case the machine and its operator have to perform the task, in the former case the trainee can consciously co-operate. From our point of view we are not concerned, *in the first place*, with whether the trainee is co-operating or whether the machines are operating well. We are concerned with examining the actual output, and how closely it conforms to a given specified type. If as a result of such an examination we find it does not so conform we can then turn to examine the reason. This may indicate, on the one hand, that the machines are not operating well or have developed a fault, or, on the other hand, that the system of training for the marksman or the operators may not be uniform, or they may not be co-operating adequately.

Suppose a factory is producing metal rods 0·5″ in diameter. Every engineer knows that it is impossible to obtain rods *exactly* 0·5″ in diameter along its whole length. To say, therefore, just baldly, that the diameter must be 0·5″ has no practical meaning ; the uses to which the rod is to be put enable those who specify the size to say what deviation may be allowed ; it must not be more than, say, 0·51″, nor less than 0·49″. A series of " go " and " not-go " gauges, for example, will enable one to decide if the diameter falls within the required limits. We can therefore draw a chart (Fig. 26) to illustrate the results of such tests; the position of the points indicate the diameters of the rods as

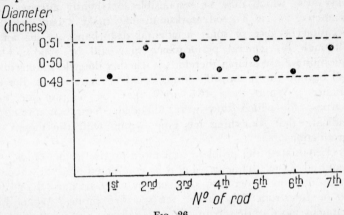

FIG. 26

measured by the gauges, and it will be seen that such a set would be regarded as satisfactory because all the points lie within the limits of specification. Now consider Fig. 27.

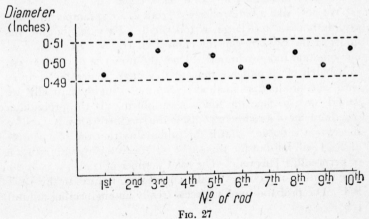

FIG. 27

In this set of ten diameters two fall outside the limits. Is this satisfactory? What does this question mean? It is clear that in the production of these rods all sorts of accidental factors may arise which may be responsible for slightly altering the diameter, just as a good marksman may make a bad shot on occasion because of some accidental disturbance to his aim, although his general performance may still be good. The question we are asking, therefore, is whether these deviations that fall outside the permissible limits could be regarded as due to chance. While these two rods may be no use for the purpose for which they were intended, does their presence indicate that something has gone wrong with the means of production?

Let us state the problem in a more precise form. Rods are required of $0.5''$ diameter. Let it be considered that the process of production is operating satisfactorily when no more than 1 in 10 of these rods falls outside the specified limits. When this happens more or less regularly we shall say the production is *stable*. This means that the probability of any rod, chosen at random, being of the wrong size is $p = \frac{1}{10}$. With such a stable system in operation we keep plotting a chart of the type shown in Fig. 27. This chart we call a *control chart*.

We now take a batch of, say, 20 rods as a test sample and find, say, 4 that are too large or too small. They fall outside the limits of the two lines in the control chart. We can now state our question more definitely. Does the presence of these 4 rods in a batch of 20 indicate that, at this stage, something is amiss with our production method? Stating it mathematically we would have to face the following problem. If the probability of a diameter of a rod being outside the specified range is $\frac{1}{10}$ when the system is stable, what is the probability that out of a sample of 20, 4 will fall outside this range? This is a direct application of Bernouilli's Theorem. The total number of trials $(= n)$ is 20. The number of successes (really engineering failures in this case) is 4. The probability of a success (really an engineering failure) is $p = \frac{1}{10}$.

Thus the probability of 4 out of a batch of 20 falling by chance outside this range

$$= \frac{20!}{4! \, 16!}\left(\frac{1}{10}\right)^4\left(\frac{9}{10}\right)^{16}$$
$$= 0\cdot09.$$

It follows that the chance of this happening by accident is 9 in 100 or the odds are 91 to 9 (*i.e.* about 10 to 1) against it happening by chance. These are heavy odds, and one would be inclined to be suspicious of this effect being due to chance. If such a situation arises in practice, a careful organizer will immediately proceed to a closer examination by taking further samples of the rods produced, in further batches of 20. If the odds against it happening by chance are maintained at that level, the result looks significant and a deeper examination of the machinery of production seems to be indicated.

As we have said the problem may not be the production of a standardized mechanical article ; it may be the training of marksmen or bomb-aimers. The limits will then be set by what is regarded as " hitting the target."

Exercise :

Let us suppose that a trained marksman is regarded as efficient when 7 out of 8 shots fall within a given ring. A trained marksman fires 12 shots, of which 4 fall outside the ring. What is the probability that his marksmanship is still unimpaired?

In practice it is obviously better to take as many samples as possible, but this raises the difficulty that the number of points which have to be plotted increases enormously. To overcome this the samples are taken in batches, say 5 at a time, and the *range of variation of each batch* is plotted as a vertical line.

For this purpose one requires only the two extreme members of each batch, the thickest and the thinnest rod. If the lines lie within the limits of specification the production, of course, is stable.

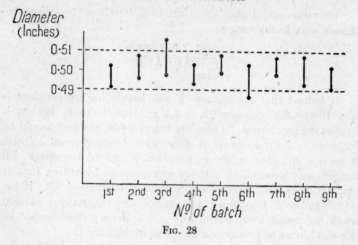

Fig. 28

For these types of criterion it should be noticed that the only testing instruments are of the " go " and " not-go " gauge type ; for all we have been concerned with has been the question whether the samples or sample batches taken fall within certain upper and lower limits.

This method of testing whether a production process remains stable has certain special points in it that require consideration. How many samples, for example, should be taken to test whether a given lot comes up to specification ? This will depend clearly on the size of the lot itself, but it will depend also on the percentage of those that are expected to be defective. Moreover, the question of the uniformity of the lot, how they are distributed about the specified size, becomes of importance, for the sample must not be so small as to allow of the possibility of its " accidental " goodness or badness vitiating our judgment. These are questions into which we cannot enter here, and reference should be made to special discussions on this particular method of checking and controlling quality.*

* See, for example, *The Bell System Technical Journal*, vol. xx (1941), pp. 1–61

Let us now consider our successive batches of samples from a slightly different standpoint.

Let us suppose that large quantities of the material we are producing have been carefully examined and measured, that the average value of this measurement is $\bar{X}$, and that the standard deviation of all the material when in stable production is found to be σ. It has been proved (Chapter VI) that if the errors are accidental, the standard deviation of the averages of successive samples of size n will be $\sigma/\sqrt{n}$.

It can also be shown that if a large series of measurements give a distribution curve, roughly of the Gaussian type, and if we derive a new set of numbers from them by taking the averages of batches of any number, say 5, then the distribution curve for the averages lies much more closely to a Gaussian distribution curve than the original set. This we have already illustrated in examples on page 38.

There is another point. If we have a large mass of measurements and we take equal groups of these and find the average in each case, the average of the result is the same as the average of the total bulk. This also has been in illustrated in Chapter V.

We assume now as stated that these values of the average of each batch show a distribution curve of the Gaussian type. Now, from Chapter XIII it can be seen that in any Gaussian distribution 99.8 per cent. of the population will fall within a distance of 3.09σ on each side of the average for the whole population. Thus 99.8 per cent. of the means of a large number of samples each of size n drawn from a normal population will fall in the range

$$\bar{X} + \frac{3.09\sigma}{\sqrt{n}} \quad \text{to} \quad \bar{X} - \frac{3.09\sigma}{\sqrt{n}}$$

where $\bar{X}$ is the average value for the whole population, which of course is also the average of the average value for each batch of n, and σ is the standard deviation for the whole population. This means in effect that in practice every value of the average of each batch of n should fall inside this range. Again, in any

Gaussian distribution 95 per cent. of the population will fall within a distance of 1.96σ on each side of the average for the whole population. Thus for the means of a large number of samples each of size n, drawn from a normal population, 95 per cent. will fall in the range

$$\bar{X} + \frac{1.96\sigma}{\sqrt{n}} \quad \text{to} \quad \bar{X} - \frac{1.96\sigma}{\sqrt{n}}.$$

We can think of it in this way :

Imagine a horizontal line drawn on a chart, at a distance $\bar{X}$ from the x axis. Then if we plot on this chart the actual measurement of each article produced, to standard size, the points will fall exactly on this line if each article were absolutely correct. But since accidental deviations do occur, the points are thrown above or below this line. If this were not so, the standard deviation of the mass of material produced under conditions regarded as satisfactory would be zero instead of σ. Now if instead of the measurement of each article, we take the average measurement of batches of n and plot these on the chart, then practically all the points, viz. 99.8 per cent. of them, ought to fall within a band $3.09\sigma/\sqrt{n}$ above $\bar{X}$, and $3.09\sigma/\sqrt{n}$ below $\bar{X}$. The width of the band, in fact, is $6.18\sigma/\sqrt{n}$.

In the same way 95 per cent. of these averages ought to fall within a band stretching from $1.96\sigma/\sqrt{n}$ above $\bar{X}$, to $1.96\sigma/\sqrt{n}$ below $\bar{X}$. The width of this band then is $3.92\sigma/\sqrt{n}$.

It is obvious that a simple chart of this nature might be used to provide a first check on whether a system of production, once established, is continuing to function effectively. For example, suppose rods of metal are being produced 12 in. in length, and that the variations that occur under satisfactory stable conditions are such as to give a standard deviation of 0.004 in. This would mean that in the past 99.8 per cent. of the rods differed from 12 in. by less than 3.09×0.004 in. either way—that is, by 0.0124 in.

It would also mean that 95 per cent. of the rods differed

from 12 in. by less than 1.96×0.004 in. either way—that is, by 0.008 in.

These would be characteristics of what we have deemed to be a stable system of production. A first test, therefore, on the persistence of stability in production would be to enter a record of the length of *each new rod* as it is produced, satisfying ourselves :

(1) that practically all (99.8 per cent.) fall within the band 12 ± 0.0124 in. ;

(2) that no less than 95 per cent. fall within the band 12 ± 0.008 in.

This is, however, rarely a practical thing to do, as must be obvious under conditions of large-scale production. Other alternatives have therefore to be sought. One might, for example, take every tenth rod, measure it, and place the result on the chart. Or one might take a batch of, say, 4 at regular intervals and deal with these, each as a unit. In that case, since we have to deal with $\sigma/\sqrt{n}$ instead of σ, and since $n = 4$ we would have the modified criteria :

(1) Practically all the averages of the batches of 4 (99.8 per cent.) fall within a band
$12 \pm 3.09 \times 0.004/\sqrt{4} = 12 \pm 0.0061$ in.

(2) No less than 95 per cent. of the averages of the batches of 4 fall within a band
$12 \pm 1.96 \times 0.004/\sqrt{4} = 12 \pm 0.0039$ in.

This would, therefore, provide a first test on whether the system of production was functioning stably.

But would it be a crucial test ? If all the points fall within these limits in the expected proportion, would this indeed mean that no change was occurring in the final product ? That this test in itself cannot suffice is obvious if we remember that each point really represents the average of four measurements.

Each of these might separately fall well outside the band within which they are required to fall (say two well above and two well below), and yet the average might still satisfy the necessary requirement. If this were to happen, of course, it would mean that a change was occurring in the standard deviation.

The appearance of such a form of instability in the scheme of production could be detected by maintaining an additional record—that of the *range* of each batch of samples. In each group of four there will be a longest and a shortest. The difference between these will represent the *spread* or *range* of the sample. It is clear that in any Gaussian distribution the range or spread of samples of any number, say 4, will have an average value. There will be an average range for batches of four samples ; and a record of the successive ranges, if maintained on a chart, should be about this average. If they begin to drift too far from the average, this will mean again that a change is taking place in the stability of the production process. It will mean that rods are being produced some of which are too long and some too short, even though the average length of the batch is still not far removed from the correct value.

How are we to know what variation is allowable in the range, if we are still to regard the production process as stable ? To answer this question we would require to make a mathematical study of the various ranges that would be obtained by choosing all the possible combinations of batches of 4 from a large group showing a Gaussian distribution in their lengths, about the average length. By this means a new distribution or a probability curve can be worked out showing the frequency or the probability with which various ranges may occur. It then becomes possible to treat this probability curve in precisely the same way as the original Gaussian curve was treated. That is to say, it becomes possible to assert that a certain percentage of the ranges found from the successive batches of 4 samples should lie within a certain band on each side of the average range, if these successive batches are being produced under stable conditions.

It is not possible in this book, from the elementary mathematical treatment we have presented, to derive the required percentage of the ranges that fall within various bands about the average range. We shall restrict ourselves merely to the following statement :

If, under stable production, the ranges of successive batches have been found to give an average range of $\bar{w}$, then no future batch should show a range outside the limits $\bar{w}$ to $D\bar{w}$ where D is a fixed number depending only on the size of the batches. In the present discussion we have continually spoken of the batch as composed of 4 members, but this is obviously not necessarily the case. For many purposes it is a convenient number to work with, but it is not necessarily so. In many cases 10 may be a better size for each batch. The value of D has been calculated on theoretical grounds for batches of size n and below we give these values of D for such a series of values of n.

n	2	3	4	5	6	7	8	9	10
D	3·52	2·58	2·26	2·08	1·97	1·90	1·84	1·79	1·75

Scheme of operation

We have thus been led to the following conclusions as a guide to decide whether a production process continues to remain stable once it has been established.

1. Determine the average value of the particular measurements with which the process is concerned. Call this $\bar{X}$. This, of course, should be the measurement which the process is expected to produce if it were functioning perfectly. It is the designed value. In practice it is found by measurement of every piece produced during an extended period when production is stable.

2. Determine the standard deviation of the particular measurements which the process has actually been producing when it has been functioning correctly and stably. This is σ.

3. The average value of every sample batch of number n should lie between $\bar{X} + 3\sigma/\sqrt{n}$ and $\bar{X} - 3\sigma/\sqrt{n}$.

Thus on a chart we draw a line parallel to the horizontal axis at distance $\bar{X}$ from that axis. On each side of it we draw a line at distance $3\sigma/\sqrt{n}$. As the average of each batch is measured the point corresponding to this average should be plotted on this diagram, and should fall within the upper and lower lines. If a point falls outside this range, there is an immediate indication that something may have gone wrong with the productive scheme. Other batches should immediately be examined and the source of the deviation traced.

4. A sharper test is to draw two lines parallel to the horizontal axis at distances $1 \cdot 96\sigma/\sqrt{n}$ from the average value. Then at least 95 per cent. of the points found from batches of n by taking their average should fall within this narrower band. Again, as soon as there is evidence that this condition is being broken, steps should be taken to discover the cause.

5. Determine the average value of the range of a large number of samples—the difference between the largest and the smallest in each batch. The average of these ranges, $\bar{w}$, is represented by the horizontal axis. This line should however be drawn on another chart just below the previous one.

6. At a distance $D\bar{w}$, where D is given in the foregoing table for each value of n, the size of the batch, another line is drawn parallel to the horizontal axis. As the range of each succeeding batch is found, its difference from the average $\bar{w}$ should be plotted on the chart, and should one of these points lie farther away from the axis than this line, then there is immediate indication that a shift is taking place in the range. The variations from one article to the next would appear to be too great, and this is a danger signal that the production process is moving away from its stable position.

Thus there are in effect so far two different tests to act as criteria in deciding whether the process continues to retain its stability in production, or whether it is deviating from that happy state.

There is one last additional criterion to which attention must be directed. The control lines we have suggested are derived from theoretical considerations. They lay down certain deviations from the average both of measurement and of range of samples that must not be exceeded. There are, however, other considerations of a very practical nature that may set even narrower bounds to these limits. When a certain measurement, say for the lengths of rods, is specified, it is understood of course that there will be a variation from one to the next in actual production. In the specification such a variation is consciously allowed for in the sense that a specified tolerance is set down, an upper and a lower bound is set to the measurement, and satisfactory production demands that no more than a certain small percentage shall diverge so far from the true value as to fall outside this range of tolerance. If we write, therefore, that the upper and the lower bounds of the tolerance are represented by T_U and T_L, then we can meet this requirement by the demand that the average sample range $\bar{w}$ shall be no more than a certain fraction of the tolerance range, viz $T_U - T_L$. If L is this fraction, then we require that

$$\bar{w} \text{ shall be less than } L(T_U - T_L).$$

The number L will, of course, depend again on n the size of the sample batch. Below we give the values of L for each value of n.

n	2	3	4	5	6	7	8	9	10
L	0·18	0·27	0·33	0·37	0·41	0·44	0·46	0·48	0·50

In this chapter an attempt has been made to outline the basis for an understanding of quality control in its application to production. The detailed types of chart that should be produced to apply these principles in any given case in a factory must depend to a large extent on the nature of the particular circumstances in that factory. Many varieties of such charts have already been suggested and tried out. The subject from the practical standpoint is still in process of being developed, and the charts that already in operation are likely to be modified as further experience is gained. There is no doubt, however, that quality control has found a permanent place in every scientifically run factory. For that reason we have restricted this chapter to a consideration of the basic principles, and have refrained from giving any of the special forms of chart now in use. These will be found in publications dealing specially with the subject of quality control rather than with the more general question of statistics.

The introduction of quality control, however, marks a revolutionary step in industrial production. In the past inspection has been restricted practically to the rôle of removing from the material produced those members that have been discovered not to satisfy the necessary requirements. The special feature of quality control lies in the fact that it replaces this negative form of inspection by something much more positive. It is a method for maintaining a watchful eye on the process in operation and interpreting the signs so that at the first indication of faulty operation action can be taken to rectify the fault, rather than action being reserved merely for a removal of the defective units. Moreover, even under the older system inspection could rarely be 100 per cent. Under modern conditions of large-scale production 100 per cent. inspection is even rarer. Quality control accepts the fact that 100 per cent. is in general impracticable, accepts the fact that a certain proportion of the units produced may be defective, and deliberately sets out a method for ensuring that this proportion shall not be exceeded. It is therefore an integral part of any system of conscious planning of industrial production. For that reason quality control must find a permanent place in the production process.

EXERCISES

1. In a large quantity of rods it is stated that 99% fall within the tolerance limits. In a sample of 100 it is found that 4 fall outside the limits. Show that the odds are nearly 70 to 1 against this occurring by accident.

2. If in a further batch of 100 there are 2 outside the limits, show that the total odds are now reduced to 32 to 1 nearly.

CHAPTER XV

THE LIMITATIONS OF NORMAL STATISTICAL ANALYSIS

In the foregoing chapter on quality control, it is very evident that the circumstances to which statistical methods can most effectively be applied correspond to a condition of equilibrium. By this we mean that we are dealing with a process that has settled down to a stable situation, and that fluctuations that do occur represent merely small accidental deviations from that stable position. An examination, for example, of the standard of marksmanship of an individual, or of a group of people, is necessarily a different matter from an examination of the rate of progress of their shooting capacity. Change of this nature has to be studied as something in itself, although the details may frequently be made more precise by the foregoing statistical analysis. In the study of quality control we have seen how such methods enable us to recognize that changes, perhaps even very rapid changes, may be imminent. As soon as this happened, we saw how important it was to turn away from the statistics to an accurate examination of the causes of the change itself. There is a fundamental point in this that is of importance to us in that it brings out certain limitations in the Gaussian Law that we must recognize, since we have been using it as a standard against which to gauge statistical data.

The Gaussian distribution was derived on the assumption that the errors or deviations are themselves composed of a large number of very small deviations, some working in a positive direction, others in a negative direction. This standard then has a value and a utility in relation to a certain class of case. Where, however, these assumptions are not valid, the Gaussian Law may be irrelevant.

Let us illustrate with a simple example. A complicated machine like an aeroplane engine may fail because any one of a certain number of parts may fail. There may not be many such parts, but the point is that the whole system goes out if one and one only fails, for each part is vital to the functioning of the whole. Now each one of these parts may be accurate according to engineering specifications, and deviations from the " absolute " in each part may vary according to the Gaussian Law. It does not follow at all that the failure of the whole system in this case will occur with a frequency that varies according to the Gaussian Law. Suppose a system consists of two components only that may fail when the whole structure is subjected to test. Let these be A and B. We have to bear in mind that A and B in combination will fail if either A or B fails.

Case 1.—Let us suppose that A and B are designed to stand up to two months' stress separately, but that each might fail separately at the end of 1 month, or even last as long as 3 months ; that it is twice as likely that A or B will fail at the end of 2 months as after 1 or 3 months. Thus we have the following frequency tables for A and B :

A fails after . .	1 month	2 months	3 months
With Frequency .	1	2	1
B fails after the same intervals with Frequency . . .	1	2	1

Let us find the probability that the combined system will fail after 1 month.

This is the probability that A will fail after 1 month + probability that A will *not fail* after 1 month but B *will fail* after 1 month. Thus the probability that the system will fail after 1 month

$$= \tfrac{1}{4} + (1 - \tfrac{1}{4}) \times \tfrac{1}{4}$$
$$= \tfrac{1}{4} + \tfrac{3}{16}$$
$$= \tfrac{7}{16}$$

Again, the probability that the system will not fail until two months have elapsed

= probability that A will fail in two months but B will not fail in the first month

+ probability that A will fail in the third month but B will fail in the second

$$= \tfrac{2}{4} \times \tfrac{3}{4} + \tfrac{1}{4} \times \tfrac{2}{4} = \tfrac{8}{16}.$$

Finally, the probability that the system will not fail until the third month

= probability that A will fail in the third month and B will fail in the third month

$$= \tfrac{1}{4} \times \tfrac{1}{4} = \tfrac{1}{16}.$$

Taking the total number of possibilities as 16, it follows that the frequency of failure for the system as a whole is

	1 month	2 months	3 months
Frequency . .	7	8	1

The average life of such a system therefore is

$$(7 \times 1 + 8 \times 2 + 1 \times 3)/(7 + 8 + 1) = 26/16 = 1 \cdot 625 \text{ mths.}$$

instead of 2 months as for each of the constituent parts. More important still, the probability of failure in the first month has risen from $\tfrac{1}{4}$, i.e. $\tfrac{4}{16}$ to $\tfrac{7}{16}$, while the probability of failure being delayed until the third month has fallen from $\tfrac{1}{4}$ to $\tfrac{1}{16}$.

Case 2.—Suppose that the two constituent elements A and B are designed to stand up to $2\tfrac{1}{2}$ months' stress but that individual elements may vary from 1 to 4 months in the following way :

A or B fails after	1 month	2 months	3 months	4 months
Frequency	1	3	3	1

We assume that B belongs to a set showing precisely the same characteristics. Note that the distribution in this and the foregoing case is the Binomial distribution. Corresponding to these frequencies the probabilities are of course $\tfrac{1}{8}$, $\tfrac{3}{8}$, $\tfrac{3}{8}$, $\tfrac{1}{8}$. We can now write down the probability of failure of the combined system after 1, 2, 3, and 4 months.

Thus the system will fail in 1 month if (i) A fails in the first month irrespectively of what B does ; (ii) A does not fail in the first month but B fails in that month.

Thus probability of failure in the first month is

$$\tfrac{1}{8} + (1 - \tfrac{1}{8})\,\tfrac{1}{8} = \tfrac{15}{64}.$$

In the same way the system will fail in the second month if

(i) A fails in the second month and B does not fail in the first ;
(ii) A does not fail in the first or second months and B fails in the second month.

Thus the required probability is

$$\tfrac{3}{8} \times (1 - \tfrac{1}{8}) + (1 - \tfrac{1}{8} - \tfrac{3}{8}) \times \tfrac{3}{8} = \tfrac{21}{64} + \tfrac{12}{64} = \tfrac{33}{64}.$$

In the same way the probabilities of failure in the third and in the fourth months are $\tfrac{15}{64}$ and $\tfrac{1}{64}$.

The average time of failure is

$$(15 \times 1 + 33 \times 2 + 15 \times 3 + 1 \times 4)/64 = \tfrac{130}{64} = 2{\cdot}03 \text{ mths.}$$

instead of 2·5 months as for the constituent elements. Moreover, the probability of failure in the first month has almost doubled and the probability of failure in the first two months has increased by 50 per cent. Failure in the fourth month has diminished from $\tfrac{8}{64}$ to $\tfrac{1}{64}$.

In both these cases there has been a shift of the symmetrical curve—itself nearly of Gaussian type—towards the earlier end, and a sharp fall at the later end. The movement is away from the Gaussian distribution. It is possible to generalize this type of problem in which with two elements any initial probability distribution is given for each of the two elements.

Case 3.—What happens when more than two elements are present, and failure in any one implies failure in the whole system ?

Consider a structure consisting of three elements, each satisfying this same frequency distribution. This time we will set it out in terms of probabilities as follows :

Period until failure	1 month	2 months	3 months
Probability of failure $\begin{cases} \\ \\ \\ \end{cases}$ A	$\frac{1}{4}$	$\frac{1}{2}$	$\frac{1}{4}$
B	$\frac{1}{4}$	$\frac{1}{2}$	$\frac{1}{4}$
C	$\frac{1}{4}$	$\frac{1}{2}$	$\frac{1}{4}$

Probability of failure at 1 *month*

= probability that A fails at 1 month,

+ probability that A does not fail then but B fails then,

+ probability that A does not fail, B does not fail, but C fails at 1 month,

$$= \tfrac{1}{4} + \tfrac{3}{4} \times \tfrac{1}{4} + \tfrac{3}{4} \times \tfrac{1}{4} + \tfrac{3}{4} \times \tfrac{3}{4} \times \tfrac{1}{4} = \tfrac{37}{64}.$$

Probability of failure at 2 *months*

= probability that A fails at 2 months while B and C do not fail at 1 month,

+ probability that A fails at 3 months while B fails at 2 months with C not failing at 1 month,

+ probability of A failing at 3 months, B failing at 3 months, while C fails at 2 months,

$$= \tfrac{1}{2}(1 - \tfrac{1}{4})(1 - \tfrac{1}{4}) + \tfrac{1}{4} \times \tfrac{1}{2}(1 - \tfrac{1}{4}) + \tfrac{1}{4} \times \tfrac{1}{4} \times \tfrac{1}{2}$$
$$= \tfrac{9}{32} + \tfrac{3}{32} + \tfrac{1}{32} = \tfrac{13}{32}.$$

Probability of failure at 3 *months*

= probability that A fails at 3 months, B at 3 months, and C at 3 months

$$= \tfrac{1}{4} \times \tfrac{1}{4} \times \tfrac{1}{4} = \tfrac{1}{64}.$$

Thus the respective probabilities are

1 month	2 months	3 months
$\frac{37}{64}$	$\frac{26}{64}$	$\frac{1}{64}$

Check.—The sum of these probabilities is 1.

Thus the frequencies of failure are proportional to

	1 month	2 months	3 months
Frequency	37	26	**1**

We notice at once that the frequency distribution for the complete system (A B C) is very different from that for each of the components A, B, C, and this is brought out clearly in Fig. 29 where the frequency for A, B, or C in 64 cases is given in the same diagram as that for A B C in 64 cases. While that for each of the constituent parts rises to its maximum at two months and then falls, that for the combined system falls steadily throughout, the most frequent time of failure being 1 month

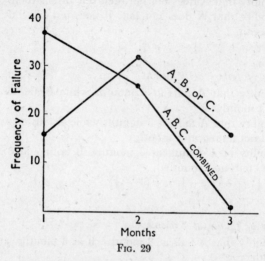

Fig. 29

instead of 2 months as in the case of the constituent parts, the average time of failure being reduced from 2 months to $1\frac{7}{16}$ months. Moreover, since the distribution diagram for the combined system is not even approximately symmetrical about the mean, the latter has little significance in the interpretation of the results. This in itself brings out how far removed the final frequency curve is from anything of a Gaussian nature.

The illustrations we have taken have been especially chosen in order to bring out the importance of examining the precise nature of the problems that are treated in order not lightly to assume that the distribution is necessarily of the Gaussian type. It is clear that if the Gauss Law of Error is to be taken as the standard against which to judge the meaning of a collection of data, the conclusions we draw as regards the probability of occurrence of deviations will be false if the data do not approximately conform to the Gauss Law. The first step, therefore, is to set out the distribution curve and settle whether it is approximately symmetrical about the average. As a general rule it can be said that if this condition appears to be satisfied it is reasonable to assume that the data can be analysed by comparison with the Gaussian curve. If, however, the data are not sufficient to enable one to say definitely that the distribution curve is approximately symmetrical about the average, then one must rely on a deeper knowledge of the nature of the problem studied. For example, it is reasonable to accept the Gaussian Law as a basis for examining errors of observation or deviations from a standardized process of production—provided, of course, care has been taken to eliminate all systematic errors that might enter. On the other hand, special classes of problems that involve " catastrophic " effects of the type discussed in this chapter cannot be lightly accepted as conforming to the Gaussian type, and such cases must receive special and detailed investigation by other methods such as those indicated here.

It is, however, not only with respect to cases of catastrophic instability that a difference may show itself from the Gaussian symmetrical distribution. Consider again, for example, the case of the Bernoulli distribution, a particular form of which we have already considered in earlier parts of this book. When the probability of a single event is $\frac{1}{2}$, the probability distribution shows symmetry about the mean and the mode, both of which coincide. Hence it is possible to represent such a distribution with considerable accuracy by means of the Gaussian Law provided of course it is interpreted with understanding. The situation is different, however, when p is not equal to $\frac{1}{2}$, for then the probability curve loses its symmetry and shows a certain *skewness*.

The probability of r successes in a particular set of n trials is

$$\frac{n!}{r!(n-r)!} \, p^r(1-p)^{n-r}$$

Thus, suppose $p = \frac{1}{5}$ and $n = 5$, the successive values of the ordinates for $r = 0, 1, 2, 3, 4, 5$ are

$$\left(\tfrac{4}{5}\right)^5, \; 5\left(\tfrac{1}{5}\right)\left(\tfrac{4}{5}\right)^4, \; 10\left(\tfrac{1}{5}\right)^2\left(\tfrac{4}{5}\right)^3, \; 10\left(\tfrac{1}{5}\right)^3\left(\tfrac{4}{5}\right)^2, \; 5\left(\tfrac{1}{5}\right)^4\left(\tfrac{4}{5}\right), \; \left(\tfrac{1}{5}\right)^5$$

$$\text{or} \quad \frac{1024}{5^5}, \; \frac{1280}{5^5}, \; \frac{640}{5^5}, \; \frac{160}{5^5}, \; \frac{20}{5^5}, \; \frac{1}{5^5}$$

Here it is clear that the most probable value occurs at $r = 1$, and the curve is drawn up towards the origin falling rapidly off as one moves outwards to larger values of r.

It is not, therefore, a good approximation to the shape of a normal frequency curve. Nevertheless the average value of r given in general by np occurs at $r = 1$, which is also the mode. Thus although the mode and the mean coincide, symmetry is absent.

When, however, n becomes larger and larger the skewness gradually disappears and the distribution approaches nearer to that of a normal frequency curve.

POISSON'S DISTRIBUTION

Suppose an event occurs on the average m times in n trials, so that we may take $p = m/n$ as the probability of its occurrence. We will suppose that it is a rare event so that p is very small. The mathematically extreme case would correspond to $m(= np)$ remaining finite as n increases indefinitely and p becomes correspondingly small.

Stated otherwise, we can say that a certain population contains p, a small proportion, of defective members. We ask for an estimate of the probability that there will be r defective members in a large batch of size n. If m is the mean number that occurs, then $m = np$.

Again the probability of r successes in n trials is

$$\frac{n!}{r!\,(n-r)!}\,p^r(1-p)^{n-r}$$

$$=\frac{n(n-1)\,(n-2)\,\ldots\,(n-r+1)}{r!}p^r(1-p)^{n-r}$$

$$=\frac{np(np-p)\,(np-2p)\,\ldots\,(np-\overline{r-1}p)}{r!\,(1-p)^r}(1-p)^{\frac{1}{p}\cdot np}$$

$$=\frac{m(m-p)\,(m-2p)\,\ldots\,(m-\overline{r-1}p)}{r!\,(1-p)^r}\left\{(1-p)^{-\frac{1}{p}}\right\}^{-m}$$

Now when p is small and r is finite $(1-p)^{-\frac{1}{p}}\longrightarrow e$

$$m(m-p)\,(m-2p)\,\ldots\,\overline{(m-r-1}p)\longrightarrow m^r$$

$$(1-p)^r\longrightarrow 1$$

Thus the probability of r successes in n trials takes the form

$$\frac{m^r}{r!}e^{-m}=\frac{(np)^r}{r!}e^{-np}$$

Example : If on the average it is found that 1 per cent. of samples of a particular product is defective, then for a large sample of 1,000 for which, therefore, $p=\dfrac{1}{100}$ and $n=1,000$, $m=np=10$, the probability of there being 0, 1, 2, 3, 4 . . . etc. defective members is e^{-10}, $\dfrac{10}{1!}e^{-10}$, $\dfrac{10^2}{2!}e^{-10}$, $\dfrac{10^3}{3!}e^{-10}$, $\dfrac{10^4}{4!}e^{-10}$ . . . etc.

Exercise

Experience has shown that on the average batches of 100 shells show 5 defective specimens. What is the probability that in a given batch of 100 shells there will be 8 defective specimens ?

We notice that the sum of the probabilities in this—the Poisson Distribution as it is called—is

$$\sum_{r=0}^{\infty} \frac{m^r}{r!} e^{-m} = e^{-m} \left(1 + \frac{m}{1!} + \frac{m^2}{2!} + \frac{m^3}{3!} + \ldots \right)$$

$$= e^{-m} \times e^m = 1$$

as is to be expected.

Again the distribution is not symmetrical, although the mode occurs at $r = m$ or the integer nearest to it and below m, while the mean is of course actually m. It is therefore not a Normal Gaussian Distribution.

That the mode occurs at the integer nearest to m and above m, if m itself is not an integer, is clear, if we seek the value of r for which $\frac{m^r e^{-m}}{r!}$ is greater than the term that precedes it and the term that follows it. Thus for the mode we require :

$$\frac{m^{r-1} e^{-m}}{(r-1)!} < \frac{m^r e^{-m}}{r!} > \frac{m^{r+1} e^{-m}}{(r+1)!}$$

From this it follows that

$$r < m \quad \text{and} \quad r + 1 > m$$
$$i.e. \quad m > r > m - 1$$

Thus while the mean and the mode lie close together they do not actually coincide.

Both the asymmetrical Bernoulli distribution and the special form of the Poisson distribution are exceedingly valuable mathematical forms for special types of case, in precisely the same way as the Gaussian mathematical form has its value. When a distribution curve has been found experimentally to lack symmetry, it is worth while in the first place to examine whether the factor that is giving rise to the skewness may not be some kind of systematic effect, which from the point of view of the experiment may be classified as a systematic error. If it can then be removed by a modification of the conditions of the experiment, then the Gaussian theory may be applied with confidence. If, however, there is no such systematic error and the distribution remains non-symmetrical, the Gaussian analysis, if it is applied at all, must be applied only in a tentative form. There is no special reason why Nature should necessarily manifest itself through the Gaussian Law of Error. To attempt to force an interpretation of Nature through such a law, even if it is mathematically beautiful, can only give rise to erroneous conclusions.

EXERCISES

1. Three types of wire, A, B, C, when subjected to a certain current are found to fail on 1 in 6 occasions, 1 in 5, and 1 in 4 respectively. Show that if the three wires are connected in series and subjected to the same current the system may be expected to fail on 1 in 2 occasions.

2. More generally, if in Exercise 1 the wires of types A, B, C fail separately on 1 in n_1, 1 in n_2, and 1 in n_3 occasions, show that the system of three wires when in series may be expected to fail on $100 \left[1 - \left(1 - \dfrac{1}{n_1} \right) \left(1 - \dfrac{1}{n_2} \right) \left(1 - \dfrac{1}{n_3} \right) \right]$ occasions out of 100.

3. In a batch of 64 rods the following errors in length are found : 1 is 3/1000 in. too long, and 1 too short by the same amount, 6 are 2/1000 in. too long, and 6 are 2/1000 in. too short, 15 are 1/1000 in. too long, and 15 are 1/1000 in. too short, while 20 are correct. All possible combinations of two rods are taken and the difference between them taken. Draw up the frequency table for these differences, and find the average difference.

ANSWERS

page 8

(2), (6, (8) unique; (1), 3, (4), (5), (7) group.

pages 17–18

(1) 4·7.   (2) (i) 486; (ii) 4·86; (iii) 5.   (3) 1/6

(4) 0·41392.   (5) 10·196.   (6) 44·51.

pages 27–29

(1) 64·55 sec.   (2) 21′ 9·4″.   (3) 8·5626.

(4) (ii) 8·875″; (iii) $37\frac{1}{2}$ per cent.; (iv) $41\frac{2}{3}$ per cent.; (v) $+5$ to -10, 55·8$\dot{3}$ per cent.

(5)

Average	3	4	5	6	7	8	9	10	11
Frequency	1	1	2	2	3	2	2	1	1

Average	4	$4\frac{2}{3}$	$5\frac{1}{3}$	6	$6\frac{2}{3}$	$7\frac{1}{3}$	8	$8\frac{1}{3}$	$9\frac{1}{3}$	10
Frequency	1	1	2	3	3	3	3	2	1	1

(6) £28.

(7) 7·25125.

pages 34–35

(1) (i) $\sqrt{\frac{2}{3}}$; (ii) $\sqrt{2}$; (iii) 2.   (2) $\sqrt{\frac{n(n-1)}{3}}$.

(3) (i) $\frac{1}{2}$; (ii) $\frac{1}{2}\sqrt{5}$; (iii) $\sqrt{\frac{35}{12}}$.   (4) $\sqrt{\left(\frac{4n^2-1}{12}\right)}$.

(6) Mean = 74·1 feet, σ = 2·47 feet.

(7) Mean = 3·87 hours, σ = 1·793 hours.

(8) Mean = 0·9573, σ = 0·08854.   (9) 1·0476.

pages 48–49

(1)

Sum	2	3	4	5	6	7	8	9	10	11	12
Frequency	1	2	3	4	5	6	5	4	3	2	1

Average sum = 7.

(2) 188, $1\frac{48}{133}$.

(3)

	f_1	f_2	f_3	f_4	f_5	f_6	f_7	f_8	f_9	f_{10}
Mean	$\frac{1}{2}$	1	$1\frac{1}{2}$	2	$2\frac{1}{2}$	3	$3\frac{1}{2}$	4	$4\frac{1}{2}$	5
Standard Deviation	$\frac{1}{2}$	$\frac{1}{2}\sqrt{2}$	$\frac{1}{2}\sqrt{3}$	1	$\frac{1}{2}\sqrt{5}$	$\frac{1}{2}\sqrt{6}$	$\frac{1}{2}\sqrt{7}$	$\sqrt{2}$	$1\frac{1}{2}$	$\frac{1}{2}\sqrt{10}$

page 57

(1) Mean = $341\frac14$.   (2) 66.   (3) 55.

(4) (i) $\sigma^2 = 11\frac54$, $\sigma_n^2 = 11\frac{5}{12}$; (ii) $\sigma^2 = 104$, $\sigma_n^2 = 26$.

pages 71–73

(1) E = 0.06095L + 0.005725, where E represents the extension, and L the load. Extension for a load of 10 lb. = 0.615.

(2) F = 0.183P + 0.408 ;

P (lb.)	11	13	15	17	19	21
F (lb.)	2.421	2.789	3.153	3.519	3.885	4.249

(3) 4.686.   (4) A = 3.974, B = − 0.403.

(5) a = 0.509, b = − 2.06.   (6) $y = -0.906 + 0.9897x^2$.

(7) A = 1.521, B = 0.49 ;

x	1	2	3	4	5
y	2.012	5.006	8.982	13.940	19.880

(9) A = 3.06, B = − 1.003.

pages 88–90

(1) 0.87.

(2) 0.095, no evidence of correlation between ages and marks.

(3) 0.89.

(4) Great Britain: mean index number = $170\frac47$, standard deviation = 38.165; U.S.A. : mean index number = $169\frac67$, standard deviation = 17.308 ; coefficient of correlation = 0.838.

(5) − 0.82.   (6) 0.96.   (7) 0.91.

pages 97–98

(1) 0.89.   (2) 0.96, 0.98.   (3) 0.70.   (4) 0.79, 0.82.

pages 112–114

(1) $\frac{4}{15}$.   (2) $\frac{1}{10}$.   (3) $\frac12$.   (4) $\frac{3}{32}$.

(5) (i) 2^{-13} ; (ii) 2^{-13} ; (iii) 2^{-12}.   (6) (i) $\frac{1}{169}$; (ii) $\frac{1}{21}$.

(7) (i) $143/2^{12}$; (ii) $429/2^{11}$; (iii) 0.103.   (8) 0.237.

(10) 0.13534.   (11) 0.335.   (12) 0.0173.

(13) $\frac{3}{25}$;

Sum	3	4	5	6	7	8	9	10	11	12	13	14	15
Probability	$\frac{1}{25}$	$\frac{2}{25}$	$\frac{2}{25}$	$\frac{3}{25}$	$\frac{3}{25}$	$\frac{3}{25}$	$\frac{2}{25}$	$\frac{2}{25}$	$\frac{3}{25}$	$\frac{2}{25}$	$\frac{2}{25}$	$\frac{1}{25}$	$\frac{1}{25}$

$\frac{3}{5}$.

(14) (i) $\frac19$; (ii) $\frac29$.   (15) $\frac{7}{27}$, $\frac{17}{27}$.   (16) $\frac{1}{64}$.   (17) $1\frac{5}{8}$.

(19) $\frac{7}{22}$.   (22) 0.665.   (23) $\frac{9}{36}$.

(24) 0.0029.   (25) $\frac{1}{6!}$, $\frac{57}{6!}$.

page 122

(1) — 0·35, no significance.

(2) True 0·542 ; by ranks 0·536 ; no significance.

(3) (i), (ii) Very significant ; chance of correlation being accidental is very much less than 1 in 100 ;

  (iii) Significant, chance of correlation being accidental is just greater than 1 in 50 ;

  (iv) Significant, chance of correlation being accidental is just less than 1 in 100.

pages 132–133

(1) 2, 2·5, 2·37, 2·44, 2·594, 2·653, 2·674, 2·684, 2·691, 2·704.

(2) 2·718.   (4) $a = \frac{1}{2}, \beta = -\frac{1}{12}$.   (5) 0·179.

(7) (i) $- e^{-x}$; (ii) $20e^{4x}$; (iii) $(n + 1)e^x$; (iv) $- 2xe^{-x^2}$;

  (v) $- 2n^2xe^{-n^2x^2}$; (vi) $(x + 1)e^x$; (vii) $(1 - 2h^2x^2)e^{-h^2x^2}$.

pages 145–146

(1) Mean = 62·487″, $\sigma = 2·5″ = 1·25$ class intervals :
  $$y = 669·05e^{-0·32x^2}$$

(2) Mean = 69·91″, $\sigma = 3·267″ = 1·089$ class intervals ;
  $$y = 439·67e^{-0·4216x^2}$$

(3) Mean = 11, $\sigma = 1·0724$,
  $$y = 11·42e^{-0·4x^2}$$
  0·62.

(4) Mean = 8·563 cm., $\sigma = 0·0175$ cm. $= 1·75$ class intervals ;
  $$y = 9·8e^{-0·163x^2}$$

page 179

(3)

Difference between pairs (in thousandths)	0	1	2	3	4	5	6
Frequency	340	792	495	220	66	12	1

Average difference = 0·001368″.

INDEX

PRINTED IN GREAT BRITAIN AT
THE PRESS OF THE PUBLISHERS